The Best of
ISAAC ASIMOV Presents

Super
Quiz

The Best of ISAAC ASIMOV Presents

Super Quiz

Ken Fisher

BARRICADE BOOKS INC.

New York

Published by Barricade Books Inc.
150 Fifth Avenue
New York, NY 10011

Printed in the United States of America.

Library of Congress Cataloging-in-Publication Data

Fisher, Ken 1936-
        The best of Isaac Asimov presents super quiz / by Ken
Fisher.
                p.   cm.
        "For the first time, the best of 15 years of questions and
answers
        have been compiled in one new volume"—Publisher's info.
                ISBN 1-56980-064-2
                1. Questions and answers. I. Asimov, Isaac, 1920–
        II. Title.
        AG195.F564 1996   95-26647
        031.02—dc20   CIP

First Printing

CONTENTS

PEOPLE 1

LITERATURE 25

LANGUAGE 37

GEOGRAPHY 51

HISTORY 69

ENTERTAINMENT 87

THEMES 123

WORDS, WORDS, WORDS 129

SPORTS 135

SCIENCE 143

MUSIC AND ART 149

MISCELLANY 157

PEOPLE

GENERAL, NUMBER ONE

Name the person from the given clue.

Freshman Level

1. The man credited as the first to sail around the world.
2. The first Englishman to sail around the world.
3. He wrote *The Origin of Species*.
4. He painted the *Mona Lisa*.
5. The English king who was beheaded.
6. The English Prime Minister during World War II.
7. A famous musical composer who became deaf.
8. Popular name for Thomas Edward Lawrence.
9. He invented a system of reading for the blind.
10. The American general known as "Blood and Guts."

1. Ferdinand Magellan
2. Sir Francis Drake
3. Charles Darwin
4. Leonardo da Vinci
5. Charles I
6. Winston Churchill
7. Ludwig van Beethoven
8. Lawrence of Arabia
9. Louis Braille
10. George S. Patton

Graduate Level

11. The discoverer of insulin.

12. He commanded the German *Afrika Korps* during World War II.
13. The Spanish artist who painted *Family of Acrobats*.
14. He wrote *Alice in Wonderland*.
15. He greatly improved the steam engine.
16. A Dutch painter who cut off his ear.
17. He tried to blow up the English Houses of Parliament.
18. The first to reach the South Pole.
19. He is said to have yelled, *"Eureka!"* when an elusive solution occurred to him in his bath tub.
20. The speed champion who drove the *Bluebird*.

11. Sir Frederick Banting and Charles H. Best
12. Erwin Rommel
13. Pablo Picasso
14. Lewis Carroll
15. James Watt
16. Vincent van Gogh
17. Guy Fawkes
18. Roald Amundsen
19. Archimedes

20. Sir Malcolm Campbell

Ph.D. Level

21. He wrote *Arms and the Man*.
22. He developed the first viable rotary internal combustion engine.
23. The author of *Emma*.
24. He was known as "Buffalo Bill."
25. The English discoverer of electro-magnetic induction.
26. The founder of psychoanalysis.
27. The English printer whose name is still used for reports of verbatim debates in Parliament.
28. The author of *Pilgrim's Progress*.
29. The leader of Hilter's *Luftwaffe*.
30. King of Egypt during the 1948 war with Israel.

21. George Bernard Shaw
22. Felix Wankel
23. Jane Austen
24. William Cody
25. Michael Faraday
26. Sigmund Freud
27. Luke Hansard

28. John Bunyan
29. Hermann Goering
30. Farouk I

GENERAL, NUMBER TWO

Freshman Level

1. He discovered penicillin.
2. A U.S. anti-Communist organization is named after him.
3. Saigon was renamed for this North Vietnamese leader.
4. Star of the TV series *The Fugitive*.
5. He Composed *Swan Lake* and *Sleeping Beauty*.
6. Retired C.B.S. anchorman who was replaced by Dan Rather.
7. This Roman slave's army was defeated in southern Italy.
8. He shot and killed Lee Harvey Oswald.
9. The first president elected from the deep South since before the Civil War.
10. Italian opera star who appeared in Broadway's *South Pacific*.

1. Sir Alexander Fleming
2. John Birch
3. Ho Chi Minh
4. David Janssen
5. Peter Tchaikovsky
6. Walter Cronkite
7. Spartacus
8. Jack Ruby
9. Jimmy Carter
10. Ezio Pinza

Graduate Level

11. This lawyer defended Lenny Bruce and Jack Ruby.
12. He authored *Dracula*.
13. She died in the F.B.I. fusillade that killed her gangster son.
14. William H. Bonney was better known as . . .
15. Israeli mentalist who claims to bend spoons with the power of his mind.
16. *I've Got a Secret* panelist who was Miss America 1945.
17. This French designer introduced the sack dress in the '50s.
18. This English hair stylist founded a network of schools and salons in New York, London, and San Francisco.
19. Winner of the best actress Oscar in 1975 for *Alice Doesn't Live Here Anymore*.
20. He introduced the first designer collection for men.

11. Melvin Belli
12. Bram Stoker
13. Kate (Ma) Barker
14. Billy the Kid
15. Uri Geller
16. Bess Myerson
17. Christian Dior
18. Vidal Sassoon
19. Ellen Burstyn
20. Pierre Cardin

Ph.D. Level

21. He was the first explorer to sight the Grand Canyon.
22. He killed Alexander Hamilton in a duel.
23. This U.S. gangster's nickname was "Legs."
24. He was the announcer on Jack Benny's radio and TV shows.
25. German author of *The Trial* and *The Castle*.
26. Journalist who traveled around the world in 72 days in 1890.
27. Commander of the Japanese fleet at Pearl Harbor.
28. He was convicted of the Lindbergh kidnapping and murder.
29. He wrote about his apprenticeship to a Yaqui sorcerer.
30. This U.S. politician drove blacks from his restaurant in defiance of federal law.

21. Francisco Coronado
22. Aaron Burr
23. John Thomas Diamond
24. Don Wilson
25. Franz Kafka
26. Nellie Bly
27. Chuichi Nagumo
28. Bruno Hauptmann
29. Carlos Castaneda
30. Lester Maddox

WHAT'S IN A NAME?
People known by a single name.

Freshman Level

1. Flamboyant U.S. pianist.
2. Greek philosopher condemned to drink hemlock.
3. Roman gladiator who led the Servile War.
4. Japanese Emperor during W.W. II.
5. The founder of Islam.
6. He led the Hebrews out of bondage in Egypt.
7. Greek writer of fables.
8. Most influential philosopher in Chinese history.
9. She rose to fame singing with Sonny Bono.
10. Best remembered for his theorem concerning right-angled triangles.

1. Liberace
2. Socrates
3. Spartacus
4. Hirohito
5. Mohammed
6. Moses
7. Aesop
8. Confucius
9. Cher
10. Pythagoras

Graduate Level

11. Author of the *Iliad* and the *Odyssey*.
12. The father of medicine.
13. He crossed the Alps with elephants.
14. Painter of the Sistine Chapel ceiling.
15. Greek mathematician who compiled the geometrical data of his time.
16. His discoveries ended the influence of Aristotle and Ptolemy on astronomy.
17. Creator of the modern Yugoslav state.
18. Singer during 1950s and 60s with backup group The Belmonts.
19. Greek philosopher who founded a school named the Lyceum.
20. Sultan of Egypt and Syria who negotiated a peace with the Crusaders.

11. Homer
12. Hippocrates
13. Hannibal
14. Michelangelo
15. Euclid
16. Galileo
17. Tito
18. Dion
19. Aristotle
20. Saladin

Ph. D. Level

21. Persian religious reformer and founder of Parsiism.
22. The first president of Indonesia.
23. Author of the *Aeneid*.
24. Actress, films include *Lost Horizon* (1937), wife of Eddie Albert.
25. Greek poet, founder of tragic drama.
26. Babylonian ruler known for his set of laws.
27. Scottish singer of the 1960s, songs include "Mellow Yellow."
28. He searched with a lantern for an honest man.
29. The famous lover of Pierre Abelard.
30. This Greek philosopher's work was in the form of dialogues and epistles.

21. Zoroaster
22. Sukarno
23. Vergil
24. Margo
25. Thespis
26. Hammurabi
27. Donovan
28. Diogenes
29. Héloïse
30. Plato

NAMES: H

Names starting with **H**.

Freshman Level

1. He wrote *Mein Kampf.*
2. He created the Muppets.
3. She received four Oscars, the last for *On Golden Pond.*
4. He wrote *A Farewell to Arms.*
5. He was Stan Laurel's partner.
6. He portrayed J.R. in *Dallas.*
7. His movies include *The Graduate* and *Tootsie.*
8. He was the master of suspense films.
9. She played TV's Rhoda.
10. He played the lead in *Ben Hur.*

1. Adolf Hitler
2. Jim Henson
3. Katharine Hepburn
4. Ernest Hemingway
5. Oliver Hardy
6. Larry Hagman
7. Dustin Hoffman
8. Alfred Hitchcock
9. Valerie Harper
10. Charlton Heston

Graduate Level

11. He wrote *Roots.*
12. He was regarded as the quietest and most spiritual of the Beatles.
13. She played the lead in the movie *Private Benjamin.*
14. His theme song is "Thanks for the Memories."
15. He founded *Playboy* magazine.
16. This U.S. labor leader disappeared in 1976.
17. *Citizen Kane* was patterned on this man's life.

18. He portrayed Caesar in *Cleopatra* (1963).
19. He played the lead in TV's *McMillan and Wife.*
20. He headed the dreaded SS in Nazi German.

11. Alex Haley
12. George Harrison
13. Goldie Hawn
14. Bob Hope
15. Hugh Hefner
16. Jimmy Hoffa
17. William Randolph Hearst
18. Rex Harrison
19. Rock Hudson
20. Heinrich Himmler

Ph.D. Level

21. This English novelist wrote *Brave New World.*
22. This German composer's works include "Water Music."
23. This composer's works include "The Way We Were."
24. She won the figure skating gold at the 1976 Olympics.
25. He played Opie on *The Andy Griffith Show.*
26. He wrote *Lost Horizon.*
27. He portrayed Luke Skywalker in *Star Wars.*
28. He shot President Reagan in 1981.
29. His books include *Demian* and *Steppenwolf.*
30. He wrote the best-selling *Kon-Tiki.*

21. Aldous Huxley
22. George F. Handel
23. Marvin Hamlisch
24. Dorothy Hamill
25. Ron Howard
26. James Hilton
27. Mark Hamill
28. John Hinckley
29. Hermann Hesse
30. Thor Heyerdahl

NAMES: L
Names starting with **L**.

Freshman Level

1. He played "the sweetest music this side of heaven."
2. This pianist is a flamboyant dresser.
3. He led the Confederate Army.
4. He painted the "Mona Lisa."
5. This Italian film star was found guilty of tax evasion in 1982.
6. She replaced Farrah Fawcett on *Charlie's Angles*.
7. He was the eldest of the Beatles.
8. She was TV's Phyllis.
9. His comic partner was Dean Martin.
10. She starred in *Deep Throat.*

1. Guy Lombardo
2. Liberace
3. Robert E. Lee
4. Leonardo da Vinci
5. Sophia Loren
6. Cheryl Ladd
7. John Lennon
8. Cloris Leachman
9. Jerry Lewis
10. Linda Lovelace

Graduate Level

11. She's a syndicated advice columnist.
12. He was known as the Sun King.
13. This German was a leader of the Protestant Reformation.
14. Her autobiography is called *A Coal Miner's Daughter*.
15. His British airline went belly up in 1982.
16. He is the coach of the Dallas Cowboys (1983).
17. She appeared in *Psycho*.
18. She was TV's Mary Hartman.
19. He was TV's Barney Miller.
20. This Canadian is a famous impressionist.

11. Ann Landers
12. Louis XIV
13. Martin Luther
14. Loretta Lynn
15. Freddie Laker
16. Tom Landry
17. Janet Leigh
18. Louise Lasser
19. Hal Linden
20. Rich Little

Ph.D. Level

21. He found evidence that human evolution was centered in Africa.
22. He was a leader of the 1960's drug culture.
23. He made an extensive exploration of Central Africa.
24. He created the fantasy world Narnia.
25. She was Andy Williams' French-born wife.
26. In 1939 he starred in *The Hunchback of Notre Dame* .
27. In 1931 he starred in *Dracula.*
28. She won five consecutive golf tournaments in 1978.
29. This Englishman helped the Arabs against Turkey in World War I.
30. She starred in the 1982 film *Frances.*

21. Louis Leakey
22. Timothy Leary
23. David Livingstone
24. C. S. Lewis
25. Claudine Longet
26. Charles Laughton
27. Bela Lugosi
28. Nancy Lopez
29. Lawrence of Arabia
30. Jessica Lange

NAMES: R
Names starting with **R**.

Freshman Level

1. His films include *The Longest Yard* and *Deliverance*.
2. He was the U.S. Vice-President from 1974 to 1976.
3. His campaign platform was "A New Deal."
4. He portrayed the Sundance Kid in *Butch Cassidy and the Sundance Kid.*
5. He starred in *Bedtime for Bonzo.*
6. He was Felix on TV's *The Odd Couple.*
7. This President backed the Panama Canal.
8. He plays Jack on TV's *Three's Company.*
9. His wife is Dale Evans.
10. She was a one-time wife of Eddie Fisher.

1. Burt Reynolds
2. Nelson Rockefeller
3. F. D. Roosevelt
4. Robert Redford
5. Ronald Reagan
6. Tony Randall
7. Theodore Roosevelt
8. John Ritter
9. Roy Rogers
10. Debbie Reynolds

Graduate Level

11. This monk influenced the last Czar and Czarina.
12. He is noted for his covers for the *Saturday Evening Post.*
13. She wrote *The Fountainhead.*
14. He was known as the Red Baron.
15. He was known as the Desert Fox.
16. He was known as the Lion-hearted.
17. Born in Brooklyn, he became one of the all-time great jazz drummers.
18. He portrayed Sherlock Holmes in the late 1930's and 40's.
19. He starred in the 1930 film *Little Caesar.*
20. He is best known for his *Believe It or Not* cartoons.

11. Grigor Rasputin
12. Norman Rockwell
13. Ayn Rand
14. Manfred von Richtofen
15. Erwin Rommel
16. Richard I
17. Buddy Rich
18. Basil Rathbone
19. Edward G. Robinson
20. Robert Ripley

Ph.D. Level

21. He starred in 1981's *Nicholas Nickleby.*
22. This French composer wrote "Bolero."
23. This French poet became a soldier, trader, gunrunner, and slaver.
24. His scoring ability helped Italy to win the World Cup in 1982.
25. This prolific Flemish painter produced more than 2,000 works.
26. This French sculptor's works include "The Thinker" and "The Kiss."
27. He was reputedly pharaoh during the Hebrew exodus from Egypt.
28. He was a Russian born virtuoso and composer.
29. This German banker founded a financial dynasty.
30. This Canadian wrote *The Apprenticeship of Duddy Kravitz.*

21. Roger Reed
22. Maurice Ravel
23. Arthur Rimbaud
24. Paoli Rossi
25. Peter Paul Rubens
26. Auguste Rodin
27. Ramses II
28. Sergei Rachmaninoff
29. Mayer Rothschild
30. Mordechai Richler

MIDDLE NAMES

All the people listed are better known by their middle name. Provide it.

Freshman Level

1. Michael Stallone	(actor)	1. Sylvester
2. Terrence McQueen	(actor)	2. Steve (Stephen)
3. William Gable	(actor)	3. Clark
4. George Newhart	(comedian)	4. Bob (Robert)
5. Marvin Simon	(playwright)	5. Neil
6. George Welles	(actor, director)	6. Orson
7. Margaret Pauley	(newscaster)	7. Jane
8. James Niven	(actor)	8. David
9. Olive Osmond	(singer)	9. Marie
10. Henry Beatty	(actor, director)	10. Warren Beatty

Graduate Level

11. Mary Fawcett	(actress)	11. Farrah
12. Charles Redford	(actor)	12. Robert
13. Eldred Peck	(actor)	13. Gregory
14. Arnold Sevareid	(newscaster)	14. Eric
15. Ernestine Russell	(actress)	15. Jane
16. Patrick O'Neal	(actor)	16. Ryan
17. Thomas Wilson	(U.S. president)	17. Woodrow
18. Stephen Cleveland	(U.S. president)	18. Grover
19. Eleanor Carter	(U.S. first lady)	19. Rosalynn
20. Alfred Runyon	(writer)	20. Damon

Ph. D. Level

21. William Crawford	(actor)	21. Broderick
22. Herbert McLuhan	(educator, writer)	22. Marshall
23. Alfred Cooke	(journalist)	23. Alistair
24. Harold Crane	(U.S. poet)	24. Hart
25. Francis Harte	(U.S. writer)	25. Bret (Brett)
26. Robert Shriver	(attorney)	26. Sargent
27. David Peckinpah	(director)	27. Sam (Samuel)
28. William Rains	(actor)	28. Claude
29. Lynn Ryan	(pitcher)	29. Nolan
30. Arthur Chamberlain	(prime minister)	30. Neville

CAPTAINS

Freshman Level

1. Captain of the pirate ship *Jolly Roger* in *Peter Pan*.
2. Commander of the starship *Enterprise*.
3. Secret identity of Billy Batson.
4. Police captain played by Hal Linden.
5. Famous Scottish pirate.
6. Captain of *HMS Bounty*.
7. Surgeon portrayed by Alan Alda on *MASH*.

8. Bad guy in McDonald commercials.
9. His life was saved by Pocahontas.
10. Their No. 1 hit was *Love Will Keep Us Together*."

1. Captain Hook
2. Captain James T. Kirk
3. Captain Marvel
4. Captain Barney Miller
5. Captain Kidd
6. Captain William Bligh
7. Captain "Hawkeye" Pierce
8. Captain Crook
9. Captain John Smith
10. Captain and Tennille

Graduate Level

11. Pirate captain who buried the treasure on *Treasure Island*.
12. Regan MacNeil's imaginary playmate in *The Exorcist*.
13. Captain of the submarine *Nautilus*.
14. Captain of the *Caine* in *The Caine Mutiny*.
15. English explorer and navigator (1728–79).
16. Nickname of Wyatt (Peter Fonda) in the film *Easy Rider*.
17. Captain played by Claude Rains in *Casablanca*.

18. Title of a novel by Rudyard Kipling (1897).
19. Errol Flynn's role in 1935 film of the same name.
20. Captain of the *Pequod* in *Moby Dick*.

11. Captain Flint
12. Captain Howdy
13. Captain Nemo
14. Captain Queeg
15. Captain James Cook
16. Captain America
17. Captain (Louis) Renaud
18. *Captains Courageous*
19. Captain Blood
20. Captain Ahab

Ph. D. Level

21. Captain portrayed by Richard Chamberlain in the TV series *Shogun*.
22. Captain of *The Flying Dutchman*.
23. Captain and owner of the *Cotton Blossom* in *Show Boat*.
24. Puppet on the *Kukla, Fran, and Ollie* TV show.
25. Secret identity of Victor (Dom De Luise) in *Cannonball Run*.
26. Comic strip character in cartoon *Wash Tubbs*.
27. Captain of the *Titanic* when she hit an iceberg.
28. Captain of the *Ghost* in *The Sea Wolf*.
29. Christopher Plummer's role in *The Sound of Music*.
30. Title of an Elton John album.

21. Captain John Blackmore
22. Captain Van Straaten
23. Captain Andy (Hawks)
24. Captain Crackie
25. Captain Chaos
26. Captain Easy
27. Captain Edward Smith
28. Captain Wolf Larsen
29. Captain von Trapp
30. "Captain Fantastic"

ADVERSARIES
Name the adversary of the given fictional character.

Freshman Level

1. Lex Luthor
2. Dr. No
3. Wile E. Coyote
4. Elmer Fudd
5. Snidely Whiplash
6. Captain Hook
7. Darth Vader
8. The Penguin
9. The Wicked Witch of the East
10. Brutus (Bluto)

1. Superman
2. James Bond
3. Roadrunner
4. Bugs Bunny
5. Dudley Do-Right
6. Peter Pan
7. Luke Skywalker
8. Batman
9. Dorothy
10. Popeye

Graduate Level

11. Ming the Merciless
12. Flattop
13. Sheriff of Nottingham
14. Wo Fat

15. Rattop
16. Sylvester Cat
17. Dr. Silvana
18. Professor Moriarty
19. The Harlequin
20. Boris Badenov

11. Flash Gordon
12. Dick Tracy
13. Robin Hood
14. Detective Steve McGarrett
15. Fearless Fosdick
16. Tweety Pie
17. Captain Marvel
18. Sherlock Holmes
19. The Green Lantern
20. Rocky and Bullwinkle

Ph. D. Level

21. Captain Esteban Pasquale
22. Oil Can Harry
23. The King of Zing
24. Doctor Octopus
25. Doctor Pauli
26. The Red Skull
27. Killer Kane
28. Mordred
29. Butch Cavendish
30. Lieutenant Philip Gerard

21. Zorro
22. Mighty Mouse
23. Plastic Man
24. Spiderman
25. Captain Video
26. Captain America
27. Buck Rogers
28. King Arthur
29. The Long Ranger
30. Richard Kimble (The Fugitive)

CELEBRITIES—LAST NAMES STARTING WITH "F"

Freshman Level

1. Star of *Sanford and Son.*
2. She was one of the original angels on *Charlie's Angels.*
3. Despite his famous father's objections, he married Joan Crawford.
4. He was nicknamed "Smokin' Joe."
5. A recent president of the United States.
6. An American chess champion.
7. A blind singer-guitarist.
8. The star of *Rosemary's Baby.*
9. Star of *Columbo*
10. She starred in *The Flying Nun.*

1. Redd Foxx
2. Farrah Fawcett
3. Douglas Fairbanks, Jr.
4. Joe Frazier
5. Gerald Ford
6. Bobby Fischer
7. José Feliciano
8. Mia Farrow
9. Peter Falk
10. Sally Field

Graduate Level

11. She played Princess Leia in *Star Wars.*
12. She played a child prostitute in *Taxi Driver*
13. He directed *Damn Yankees, Pippin, Chicago,* and *Cabaret.*
14. An actor and also father of Peter and Jane.
15. She was the 1968 Olympic figure skating champion.
16. This English interviewer filmed a series of interviews with former President Richard Nixon.
17. Symbol of the Boston Pops.
18. The Italian film director of *La Dolce Vita.*
19. She was married to Tony Martin and later to Phil Harris.
20. Rock star who recorded the hit album *I'm in You.*

11. Carrie Fisher
12. Jodie Foster
13. Bob Fosse
14. Henry Fonda
15. Peggy Fleming
16. David Frost
17. Arthur Fiedler
18. Federico Fellini
19. Alice Faye
20. Peter Frampton

Ph.D. Level

21. He designed the geodesic dome.
22. Author of *The Feminine Mystique.*
23. He won the Indianapolis 500 in 1961, 1964, 1967, and 1977.
24. A past regular on *What's My Line?*
25. Her 1972 hit was "The First Time Ever I Saw Your Face."
26. He was divorced by actress Eleanor Powell.
27. Her older sister is Olivia de Havilland.
28. He starred in *Two for the Road* and the musical *Scrooge.*
29. His third wife was Rosemary Clooney.
30. A syndicated satirical cartoonist.

21. Buckminster Fuller
22. Betty Friedan
23. A. J. Foyt
24. Arlene Francis
25. Roberta Flack
26. Glenn Ford
27. Joan Fontaine
28. Albert Finney
29. Jose Ferrer
30. Jules Feiffer

CELEBRITIES — JOHN, JAMES, AND JOE

Freshman Level: John

1. Famous host of the *Tonight* show.
2. He is Charlie in *Charlie's Angels*.
3. A famous Canadian-born economist.
4. Western singer and husband of June Carter.
5. America's first orbiting astronaut.
6. "The Duke."
7. Star of the 1947 film version of *Body and Soul* and *Humoresque*.
8. A black ballad singer, whose theme song is "Wonderful, Wonderful."
9. Famous Cincinnati catcher.
10. British film star and father of Hayley.

1. Carson
2. Forsythe
3. Galbraith
4. Cash
5. Glenn
6. Wayne
7. Garfield
8. Mathis
9. Bench
10. Mills

Graduate Level: James

11. He squashed a grapefruit in Mae Clark's face.
12. Our man Flint.
13. The protagonist of *Maverick*.
14. He exploded to Broadway stardom in *Last of the Red Hot Lovers*.
15. Head of the Teamsters who disappeared.
16. English-born actor who starred in *Lolita*.
17. He played the role of Glen Miller.
18. Matt Dillon of *Gunsmoke*.
19. Sonny in *The Godfather*.
20. Black singer and "Soul Brother Number One."

11. Cagney
12. Coburn
13. Garner
14. Coco
15. Hoffa
16. Mason
17. Stewart
18. Arness
19. Caan
20. Brown

Ph.D. Level: Joe

21. He was a Prime Minister of Canada.
22. He is known as the "King of White Soul Music."
23. He was once the leader of Russia.
24. He led the Jets to a Super Bowl upset.
25. He directed *Cleopatra* and *Sleuth*.
26. An ex-ballplayer who did Mr. Coffee commercials.
27. Baseball hero turned sportscaster turned interviewer.
28. Sad-faced funny man who has guest-hosted the *Tonight* show.
29. A tycoon whose sons became major U.S. politicians.
30. Wide-mouthed comedian of the '30s.

21. Clark
22. Cocker
23. Stalin
24. Namath
25. Mankiewicz
26. DiMaggio
27. Garagiola
28. Bishop
29. Kennedy
30. E. Brown

MARRIAGES

Name the wife of each person (not necessarily still married). The first name is provided.

Freshman Level

1.	Steve Allen	Jayne	1.	Meadows
2.	John Astin	Patti	2.	Duke
3.	George Burns	Gracie	3.	Allen
4.	Roy Rogers	Dale	4.	Evans
5.	Mel Brooks	Anne	5.	Bancroft
6.	Bobby Darin	Sandra	6.	Dee
7.	Steve McQueen	Ali	7.	MacGraw
8.	Paul Newman	Joanne	8.	Woodward
9.	Allen Ludden	Betty	9.	White
10.	José Ferrer	Rosemary	10.	Clooney

Graduate Level

11.	Charles Bronson	Jill	11.	Ireland
12.	Ernie Kovaks	Edie	12.	Adams
13.	Jack Cassidy	Shirley	13.	Jones
14.	Tony Martin	Cyd	14.	Charisse
15.	George Montgomery	Dinah	15.	Shore
16.	Fernando Lamas	Esther	16.	Williams
17.	Mickey Rooney	Ava	17.	Gardner
18.	Mel Ferrer	Audrey	18.	Hepburn
19.	Charles Laughton	Elsa	19.	Lanchester
20.	Al Jolson	Ruby	20.	Keeler

Ph.D. Level

21.	Wallace Beery	Gloria	21.	Swanson
22.	Rip Torn	Geraldine	22.	Page
23.	Gig Young	Elizabeth	23.	Montgomery
24.	Moss Hart	Kitty	24.	Carlisle
25.	Fred McMurray	June	25.	Haver
26.	John Payne	Gloria	26.	DeHaven
27.	Gilbert Roland	Constance	27.	Bennett
28.	Carlo Ponti	Sophia	28.	Loren
29.	Buster Keaton	Natalie	29.	Talmadge
30.	Burgess Meredith	Paulette	30.	Goddard

WOMEN

Freshman Level

1. French actress known as the "Sex Kitten."	1. Brigitte Bardot
2. Queen of Egypt and mistress of Julius Ceasar.	2. Cleopatra
3. Empress of Russia from 1762–1796.	3. Catherine the Great
4. She was a joint discoverer of radium	4. Marie Curie
5. Peasant girl who led the French army to victories.	5. Joan of Arc
6. Queen of England during the time of Sir Francis Drake.	6. Elizabeth I
7. She overcame many handicaps to become a lecturer and scholar	7. Helen Keller
8. The first woman to swim the English Channel (1926).	8. Gertrude Ederle
9. The first women premier of Israel.	9. Golda Meir
10. Queen of Spain during Columbus' voyage.	10. Isabella I

Graduate Level

11. Famous French actress of the late 19th century.	11. Sarah Bernhardt
12. The first woman to swim the English Channel both ways.	12. Florence Chadwick
13. German actress and singer noted for her legs.	13. Marlene Dietrich
14. Actress who co-starred with W. C. Fields in *My Little Chickadee*.	14. Mae West
15. The first woman prime minister of India.	15. Indira Gandhi
16. She was the singles champion at Wimbledom from 1966–1968.	16. Billie Jean King
17. Double agent shot as a spy by the French.	17. Mata Hari
18. The all-round gymnastics winner at the 1976 Olympics.	18. Nadia Comaneci
19. Olympic figure skating champion in 1928, 1932, and 1936.	19. Sonja Henie
20. First Australian aborigine to play international tennis.	20. Evonne Goolagong

Ph.D. Level

21. French saint whose visions established Lourdes as a healing shrine.	21. Bernadette
22. Woman's rights campaigner who popularized pantaloons.	22. Amelia Bloomer
23. American novelist who wrote *The Good Earth*.	23. Pearl Buck
24. American operatic soprano of Greek parentage.	24. Maria Callas
25. She wrote stories about Peter Rabbit.	25. Beatrix Potter
26. She won the 1979 Nobel Peace Prize.	26. Mother Teresa
27. French novelist and feminist associated with Chopin.	27. George Sand
28. Kidnapped from her Berkeley apartment, she later joined her captors in committing crimes.	28. Patricia Hearst
29. She won the Olympic 100- and 200-meter freestyle swimming championships in 1976.	29. Kornelia Ender
30. Virtual ruler of France from 1560 to 1574.	30. Catherine de' Medici

PAIRS

Give the second of the pair of characters. Not all of the characters are real people.

Freshman Level

1. Cain and ...
2. Amos and ...
3. Romeo and ...
4. Antony and ...
5. Jack and ...
6. Frankie and ...
7. Abbott and ...
8. Tom and ...
9. Hansel and ...
10. Laurel and ...

1. Abel
2. Andy
3. Juliet
4. Cleopatra
5. Jill
6. Johnny
7. Costello
8. Jerry
9. Gretel
10. Hardy

Graduate Level

11. Barnum and ...
12. Johnson and ...
13. Burns and ...
14. Proctor and ...
15. Sonny and ...
16. Bob and ...
17. Stanley and ...
18. Masters and ...
19. Bergen and ...
20. Sampson and ...

11. Bailey
12. Johnson
13. Allen
14. Gamble
15. Cher
16. Ray
17. Livingstone
18. Johnson
19. McCarthy
20. Delilah

Ph.D. Level

21. Castor and ...
22. David and ...
23. Mason and ...
24. Rodgers and ...
25. Lewis and ...
26. Cupid and ...
27. Boaz and ...
28. Gilbert and ...
29. Stiller and ...
30. Damon and ...

21. Pollux
22. Bathsheeba or Goliath
23. Dixon
24. Hammerstein or Hart
25. Clark
26. Psyche
27. Ruth
28. Sullivan
29. Meara
30. Pythias

FAMOUS LOVERS

Freshman Level

1. Marc Antony and
2. Romeo and
3. Rhett Butler and
4. Robin Hood and
5. Sir Lancelot and
6. Napoleon and
7. Katharine Hepburn and
8. Richard Burton and
9. Li'l Abner and
10. Carlo Ponti and

1. Cleopatra
2. Juliet
3. Scarlett O'Hara
4. Maid Marian
5. Guinevere
6. Josephine
7. Spencer Tracy
8. Elizabeth Taylor
9. Daisy Mae
10. Sophia Loren

Graduate Level

11. Robert Browning and
12. Carole Lombard and
13. Humphrey Bogart and
14. William Randolph Hearst and
15. Edward VIII and
16. Paris and
17. Dante and
18. John Alden and
19. Yoko Ono and
20. Prince Albert and

11. Elizabeth Barrett
12. Clark Gable
13. Lauren Bacall
14. Marion Davies
15. Wallis Simpson
16. Helen of Troy
17. Beatrice
18. Priscilla
19. John Lennon
20. Queen Victoria

Ph.D. Level

21. Madame Pompadour and
22. Heloise and
23. Penelope and
24. Tristram and
25. Boaz and
26. Isis and
27. Simone de Beauvoir and
28. Heathcliff and
29. Emma Hamilton and
30. Blanche DuBois and

21. Louis XV
22. Abelard
23. Odysseus
24. Isolde
25. Ruth
26. Osiris
27. Jean-Paul Sartre
28. Cathy Linton
29. Lord Nelson
30. Stanley Kowalski

FIRST NAMES: Robert (Bob)

From the clue, give the last name of the person whose first name is Robert.

Freshman Level

1. He starred in *Baretta*.
2. This U.S. poet won a Pulitzer Prize in 1924.
3. He wrote *Treasure Island*.
4. He surrendered to Grant.
5. He was assassinated while campaigning in 1968.
6. He starred in *The Candidate* and *The Sting*.
7. He starred in the TV series *The Untouchables*
8. He starred in the TV series *Father Knows Best*.
9. He married Elizabeth Barrett.
10. He was in *The Sting* and *Jaws*.

1. Blake
2. Frost
3. Louis Stevenson
4. E. Lee
5. Francis Kennedy
6. Redford
7. Stack
8. Young
9. Browning
10. Shaw

Graduate Level

11. He starred in *Raging Bull*.
12. His films include *The Godfather* and *Apocalypse Now*.
13. He is best known for his role in *The Music Man*.
14. He is best known for his role in *The Brady Bunch*.
15. He is the best known Scottish poet.
16. He led the first expedition to reach the North Pole.
17. He is the father of modern rocketry.
18. He is best known for his role of Napoleon Solo in the TV series *Man from U.N.C.L.E.*
19. He made his broadway debut in *Camelot*.
20. This explorer perished near the South Pole.

11. DeNiro
12. Duvall
13. Preston
14. Reed
15. Burns
16. Peary
17. Goddard
18. Vaughn
19. Goulet
20. Scott

Ph.D. Level

21. He was the lead singer for Led Zeppelin.
22. He was Clarabell the Clown and Captain Kangaroo.
23. He was Britain's first Prime Minister.
24. He was the author of *I, Claudius*.
25. He starred in *Baa, Baa, Black Sheep*.
26. He starred in the TV series *I Spy*.
27. The first American to sing 500 performances at the Metropolitan Opera.
28. He wrote *The Matarese Circle*.
29. He was first to develop a practical steamship.

21. Plant
22. Keeshan
23. Walpole
24. Graves
25. Conrad
26. Culp
27. Merrill
28. Ludlum.
29. Fulton

HISTORICAL FIGURES

Freshman Level

1. He was stabbed to death on the Ides of March.
2. America is named after him.
3. The Russian leader during World War II.
4. The first Roman Catholic president of the U.S.A.
5. Author of *Das Kapital*.
6. American general who evacuated the Philippines in 1942.
7. Arab prophet and founder of Islam.
8. Aztec emperor of Mexico.
9. He was known as "Il Duce."
10. He delivered the Gettysburg Address.

1. Julius Caesar
2. Amerigo Vespucci
3. Joseph Stalin
4. John F. Kennedy
5. Karl Marx
6. Douglas MacArthur
7. Mohammed
8. Montezuma
9. Benito Mussolini
10. Abraham Lincoln

Graduate Level

11. He founded the city of Quebec.
12. A Venetian who traveled to Peking in 1275.
13. He said, "Dr. Livingstone, I presume."
14. The first to round the southern tip of Africa.
15. British prime minister noted for his appeasement of Hitler.
16. Soviet politician who brought Stalinism to an end.
17. American senator noted for anti-Communist "witch-hunts."
18. He led the "Long March" in China.
19. Queen of France who was beheaded in 1793.
20. He rallied the Free French during World War II.

11. Samuel de Champlain
12. Marco Polo
13. Henry M. Stanley
14. Bartholomeu Dias
15. Neville Chamberlain
16. Nikita Khrushchev
17. Joseph McCarthy
18. Mao Tse-Tung
19. Marie Antoinette
20. Charles de Gaulle

Ph.D. Level

21. He became president when Harding died in 1923
22. He charted New Zealand and eastern Australia.
23. His realm was the beginning of the Holy Roman Empire.
24. Mongol emperor who encouraged contacts with the west.
25. Elizabeth I had her beheaded.
26. The first prime minister of Israel.
27. Chaldean king of Babylon who built the "Hanging Gardens."
28. His flagship was named *Victory*.
29. Argentinian dictator in 1946.
30. Tsar of Russia who transformed Russia into a modern state.

21. Calvin Coolidge
22. James Cook
23. Charlemagne
24. Kublai Khan
25. Mary Stuart
26. David Ben-Gurion
27. Nebuchadnezzar II
28. Horatio Nelson
29. Juan Perón
30. Peter the Great

CHARACTERS IN THE COMICS

Freshman Level

1. He was Captain Marvel
2. What were the names of the Katzenjammer Kids?
3. She was Superman's girlfriend
4. He was Mandrake's faithful companion.
5. His girlfriend was Jane
6. Buster Crabbe played him in the movies

7. He was Batman.
8. Her dog's name was Sandy.
9. He was the Shadow.
10. He was Blondie's husband.

1. Billy Batson
2. Hans and Fritz
3. Lois Lane
4. Lothar
5. Tarzan
6. Buck Rogers, Flash Gordon, Tarzan
7. Bruce Wayne
8. Little Orphan Annie
9. Lamont Cranston
10. Dagwood Bumstead

Graduate Level

11. He was Clark Kent's young colleague and friend.
12. She lived on Paradise Island.
13. He was an affectionate parody of Dick Tracy.
14. She was Flash Gordon's girlfriend.
15. She was a voluptuous villainess in Terry and the Priates.
16. He headed a shaky airline company called Horizons Unlimited.
17. He began as a petty crook named Eel O'Brien and gained amazing stretching powers after being thrown into a vat of acid.
18. His girlfriend was Tess Trueheart.
19. He was Batman's sidekick, Robin.
20. This character never spoke, always wore a crown, and had a pointed beard.

11. Jimmy Olsen
12. Wonder Woman
13. Fearless Fosdick
14. Dale Arden
15. The Dragon Lady
16. Steve Canyon
17. Plastic Man.

18. Dick Tracy
19. Dick Grayson
20. The Little King

Ph.D. Level

21. He was Clark Kent's boss.
22. He was Buck Rogers's archfoe.
23. She was Fearless Fosdick's girlfriend.
24. He was Emperor of Mongo in *Flash Gordon*.
25. Her boyfriend was Tubby Tompkins.
26. She was a female Tarzan.

27. He was Dagwood's boss.
28. This was Blondie and Dagwood's dog.
29. He wore a black suit and a blazing crimson turban.
30. This is Hi and Lois's baby.

21. Perry White
22. Killer Kane
23. Prudence Pimpleton
24. Ming the Merciless
25. Little Lulu
26. Sheena, Queen of the Jungle
27. Mr. Dithers
28. Daisy
29. Ibis the Invincible
30. Trixie

CHARACTERS IN LITERATURE

Freshman Level

1. He tilted at windmills.
2. He was the most famous of King Arthur's knights.
3. The submarine captain in *Twenty Thousand Leagues Under the Sea*.
4. The child heroine of *Through the Looking Glass*.
5. In *The Arabian Nights* he finds a magic lamp.
6. A Titan compelled to support the vault of heaven.
7. A man of the church in Robin Hood's band.
8. He was marooned on an island.
9. He fell asleep for twenty years.
10. The musician who rid a town of rats.

1. Don Quixote
2. Lancelot
3. Captain Nemo

4. Alice
5. Aladdin
6. Atlas
7. Friar Tuck
8. Robinson Crusoe
9. Rip Van Winkle
10. Pied Piper

Graduate Level

11. He was kidnapped from his village in *Roots*.
12. Porthos and Aramis were two of the Three Musketeers; who was the third?
13. The merchant of *The Merchant of Venice*.
14. He was vulnerable in his right heel.
15. A young pickpocket in *Oliver Twist*.
16. His ghost haunts Macbeth.
17. The hero of Bunyan's *Pilgrim's Progress*.
18. The barber of *The Barber of Seville*.
19. The wife of King Arthur.
20. The heroine of *Pride and Prejudice*.

11. Kunta Kinte
12. Athos

13. Antonio
14. Achilles
15. The Artful Dodger
16. Banquo
17. Christian
18. Figaro
19. Guinevere
20. Elizabeth Bennet

Ph.D. Level

21. A sword was suspended by a hair over his head.
22. The hero of Stevenson's *Kidnapped*.
23. She was a weaver who was turned into a spider.
24. A Red Indian chief in James Fenimore Cooper's novels.
25. A close friend of the Three Musketeers.
26. A receiver of stolen goods in *Oliver Twist*.
27. The hero of *The Count of Monte Cristo*..
28. The sun melted his wings of wax.
29. The leader of the Argonauts.
30. He killed Macbeth.

21. Damocles
22. David Balfour
23. Arachne
24. Chingachgook
25. D'Artagnan
26. Fagin
27. Edmond Dantes
28. Icarus
29. Jason
30. Macduff

BLACK AMERICANS

Freshman Level

1. He had the longest reign as world heavyweight boxing champion.
2. He was the first black baseball player in the major leagues.
3. He is a pop singer of songs such as "Chances Are."
4. This writer and civil rights leader fought against the lynching of blacks. Author of *Fire in the Flint.*
5. He was the leading trumpeter in jazz history.
6. This leader of nonviolent civil rights was assassinated.
7. In 1983 he became Chicago's first black mayor.
8. He was the author of *Roots.*
9. This blind singer-composer sang, "You Are the Sunshine of My Life."
10. He won at Wimbledon in 1975.

1. Joe Louis
2. Jackie Robinson
3. Johnny Mathis
4. Walter F. White
5. Louis Armstrong
6. Martin Luther King Jr.
7. Harold Washington
8. Arthur Haley
9. Stevie Wonder
10. Arthur Ashe

Graduate Level

11. She was a "conductor" on the Underground Railroad.
12. This athlete, actor, and concert singer was blacklisted.
13. He led a revolt in Virginia in 1831.
14. He discovered many new uses for the peanut.
15. This jazz musician and composer led his own orchestra from 1923 to 1974.
16. He was the first black heavyweight boxing champion.
17. He was an innovative pianist and composer of ragtime music.
18. This advocate of black nationalism led a "Back to Africa" movement in the 1920's.
19. This baseball player was allowed into the major leagues at age forty-two.
20. This track athlete won four gold medals at the 1936 Olympics.

11. Harriet Tubman
12. Paul Robeson
13. Nat Turner
14. George Washington Carver
15. Duke Ellington
16. Jack Johnson
17. Scott Joplin
18. Marcus Garvey
19. Leroy "Satchel" Paige
20. Jesse Owens

Ph.D. Level

21. He was the U.S. ambassador to the United Nations in 1977.
22. This novelist and playwright wrote *Another Country.*
23. He was elected mayor of Los Angeles in 1973.
24. He placed the U.S. flag at the North Pole.
25. The first black elected to the Senate since the Reconstruction era.
26. Her autobiography was *Lady Sings the Blues.*
27. The executive director of the NAACP from 1955 to 1977.
28. The author of *Up from Slavery.*
29. He was the first black Supreme Court Justice.
30. He won the Nobel Peace Prize in 1950 for his mediation of the Palestine dispute.

21. Andrew Young
22. James Baldwin
23. Thomas Bradley
24. Matthew Henson
25. Edward Brooke
26. Billie Holiday
27. Roy Wilkins
28. Booker T. Washington
29. Thurgood Marshall
30. Ralph Bunche

DOCTORS

Freshman Level

1. Henry Stanley located him in Africa.
2. He was also Mr. Hyde.
3. Author of *The Cat in the Hat*.
4. He worked with Sherlock Holmes.
5. General practitioner played on TV by Robert Young.
6. This is actually a soft drink.
7. The TV series *The Fugitive* was about a pediatrician named . . .
8. He was played on TV by Richard Chamberlain.
9. He created a monster.
10. Hero of a book that won the Nobel Prize for Literature.

1. Dr. Livingstone
2. Dr. Jekyll
3. Dr. Seuss
4. Dr. Watson
5. Dr. Welby
6. Dr. Pepper
7. Dr. Richard Kimble
8. Dr. Kildare
9. Dr. Frankenstein
10. Dr. Zhivago

Graduate Level

11. The villainous opponent in the first James Bond film.
12. Vince Edwards played this doctor in a TV series.
13. Giving up a musical career, he became a medical missionary in Africa.
14. He lived in the English town of Puddleby-on-the-Marsh with many pets.
15. Bob Newhart played this Chicago psychologist.
16. The doctor in TV's *Peyton Place*.
17. He was portrayed by Peter Sellers in a movie about the bomb.
18. The doctor aboard the USS *Enterprise*.
19. He wrote the *Common Sense Book of Baby and Child Care*.
20. Two brothers, William and James, were U.S. surgeons who founded a famous clinic bearing their name.

11. Dr. No
12. Dr. Ben Casey
13. Albert Schweitzer
14. Dr. Dolittle
15. Dr. Robert Hartley
16. Dr. Rossi
17. Dr. Strangelove
18. Dr. McCoy
19. Dr. Benjamin Spock
20. Mayo

Ph.D. Level

21. He was Marcus Welby's assistant.
22. He was Ben Casey's superior at County General Hospital.
23. The mentor of Dr. Kildare, portrayed by Lionel Barrymore in the movies.
24. Richard Boone played him on TV's *Medic*.
25. English physician who discovered the circulation of blood.
26. In a 1939 horror film this mad scientist reduced the rest of the characters to midgets.
27. The Greek physician who is the father of medicine.
28. This kindly country doctor hero was played by Jean Hersholt.
29. The resident doctor at St. Swithian's Hospital played by Dirk Bogarde in the *Doctor* series.
30. He took part in the gunfight at the OK Corral.

21. Dr. Steven Kiley
22. Dr. Zorba
23. Dr. Gillespie
24. Dr. Konrad Styner
25. William Harvey
26. Dr. Cyclops
27. Hippocrates
28. Dr. Christian
29. Dr. Simon Sparrow
30. Doc Holliday

NAMES WITH INITIALS

Give the name for which the initials stand.

Freshman Level

1. J. F. Kennedy	1. John Fitzgerald
2. F. D. Roosevelt	2. Franklin Delano
3. Richard M. Nixon	3. Milhous
4. Gerald R. Ford	4. Rudolph
5. J. Edgar Hoover	5. John
6. L. B. Johnson	6. Lyndon Baines
7. Dwight D. Eisenhower	7. David
8. Harry S Truman	8. (nil)
9. F. Scott Fitzgerald	9. Francis
10. Robert E. Lee	10. Edward

Graduate Level

11. D. H. Lawrence	11. David Herbert
12. George M. Cohan	12. Michael
13. F. Lee Bailey	13. Francis
14. W. C. Fields	14. William Claude
15. C. P. Snow	15. Charles Percy
16. E. L. Doctorow	16. Edgar Lawrence
17. Lee J. Cobb	17. Jacoby
18. George C. Scott	18. Campbell
19. Edward G. Robinson	19. Goldenburg
20. J. B. Priestley	20. John Boynton

Ph.D. Level

21. Cecil B. DeMille	21. Blount
22. T. H. White	22. Terence Hanbury
23. H. B. Warner	23. Herbert Bryan
24. Y. A. Tittle	24. Yelberton Abraham
25. J. D. Salinger	25. Jerome David
26. D. W. Griffith	26. David Wark
27. A. J. Foyt	27. Anthony James
28. P. T. Barnum	28. Phineas Taylor
29. O. J. Simpson	29. Orenthal James
30. J. R. R. Tolkien	30. John Ronald Reuel

PSEUDONYMS

Provide the pseudonym. You are given the original name plus the initials of the performance name.

Freshman Level

1. Antonio Benedetto	T.B.	1. Tony Bennett
2. Milton Berlinger	M.B.	2. Milton Berle
3. James Baumgardner	J.G.	3. James Garner
4. Norma Jean Baker	M.M.	4. Marilyn Monroe
5. George Rauft	G.R.	5. George Raft
6. Frederick Austerlitz	F.A.	6. Fred Astaire
7. John Sanford	R.F.	7. Redd Foxx
8. Concetta Franconero	C.F.	8. Connie Francis
9. Greta Gustafson	G.G.	9. Greta Garbo
10. Emmett Evan Heflin	V.H.	10. Van Heflin

Graduate Level

11. Ethel Zimmerman	E.M.	11. Ethel Merman
12. Dino Crocetti	D.M.	12. Dean Martin
13. Charles Buchinski	C.B.	13. Charles Bronson
14. David Daniel Kaminsky	D.K.	14. Danny Kaye
15. Bela Blasko	B.L.	15. Bela Lugosi
16. Bernard Schwartz	T.C.	16. Tony Curtis
17. Frances Gumm	J.G.	17. Judy Garland
18. Israel Iskowitz	E.C.	18. Eddie Cantor
19. William Beedle Jr.	W.H.	19. William Holden
20. Gladys Smith	M.P.	20. Mary Pickford

Ph.D. Level

21. Allen Stewart Konigsberg	W.A.	21. Woody Allen
22. Robert Zimmerman	B.D.	22. Bob Dylan
23. Julius Garfinkle	J.G.	23. John Garfield
24. James Stewart	S.G.	24. Stewart Granger
25. Emanuel Goldenberg	E.G.R.	25. Edward G. Robinson
26. Leonard Slye	R.R.	26. Roy Rogers
27. Marion Michael Morrison	J.W.	27. John Wayne
28. Sydney Liebowitz	S.L.	28. Steve Lawrence
29. Benjamin Kubelsky	J.B.	29. Jack Benny
30. Steveland Morris	S.W.	30. Stevie Wonder

EPONYMS

Identify the person whose name lives in our language.

Freshman Level

1. He invented a close-fitting garment worn by dancers.
2. His name has come to mean an unbranded range calf or colt.
3. He discovered a process to kill bacteria in wine and milk.
4. A thick slice of tenderloin, broiled and often served with a béarnaise sauce, is named after this man.
5. He committed crimes of sexual cruelty.
6. He popularized a stabbing and cutting knife.
7. A Scottish inventor whose name became a unit of power.
8. He loved gambling so much he refused to leave the table to eat and subsequently invented a new type of meal.
9. He invented a crank-operated machine gun.
10. He invented a short-barreled large-caliber pistol.

1. Jules Léotard
2. Sam Maverick
3. Louis Pasteur
4. François Chateaubriand
5. Marquis de Sade
6. Jim Bowie
7. James Watt
8. Earl of Sandwich
9. Richard Gatling
10. Henry Deringer

Graduate Level

11. He was hired to collect rents from poor Irish tenant farmers, but they refused to deal with him.
12. He invented an engine that ran on cheap crude oil.
13. This naval surgeon thought straight gin harmed the health, so he diluted it with lime juice.
14. This blind monk invented the first true champagne.
15. He invented the "six-shooter" of the American West.
16. A U.S. statistician and public-opinion analyst.
17. He was a German general, aviator, and airship builder.
18. He convicted and punished offenders without a court of law.
19. A Norwegian official who collaborated with Hitler.
20. He invented brass and wind instruments.

11. Charles Boycott
12. Rudolf Diesel
13. Sir Gimlette
14. Dom Pérignon
15. Samuel Colt
16. George Gallup
17. Ferdinand von Zeppelin
18. Charles Lynch
19. Vidkun Quisling
20. Antoine Sax

Ph.D. Level

21. This Frenchman's name denotes a unit of electrical current.
22. Lecturer at Oxford renowned for slips of the tongue which transposed sounds, as in "off the treaten back."
23. An Italian physicist and electrical pioneer whose name denotes a unit of electromotive force.
24. He edited prudishly to produce a family edition of Shakespeare.
25. Zealous supporter of Napoleon whose name is now associated with exaggerated partiality.
26. This Russian's name, which means "the hammer," is used for a crude type of hand-thrown bomb.
27. He could derive pleasure only from being physically abused and tortured.
28. A word meaning "trousers" comes from this saint's name.
29. French finance minister ridiculed for petty economies.
30. Army meat inspector who was the first "Uncle Sam."

21. André Ampère
22. William Spooner
23. Alessandro Volta
24. Thomas Bowdler
25. Nicholas Chauvin
26. Vyacheslav Molotov
27. Leopold von Sacher-Masoch
28. Pantaleon
29. Etienne de Silhouette
30. Samuel Wilson

LITERATURE

GENERAL: NUMBER ONE

Freshman Level

1. Which character said, "To be, or not to be"?
2. He wrote *A Tale of Two Cities*.
3. He was a famous archer and outlaw of medieval England.
4. Name Charlie Brown's dog.
5. He wrote *Mein Kampf*.
6. He constructed a monster from human parts.
7. This book by Robert Louis Stevenson deals with a person with a dual personality.
8. She rode naked through the town.
9. Who was the young girl in the novel *Tom Sawyer*?
10. What do Ray Bradbury, Jules Verne, and H. G. Wells have in common?

1. Hamlet
2. Charles Dickens
3. Robin Hood
4. Snoopy
5. Adolf Hitler
6. Dr. Frankenstein
7. *Dr. Jekyll and Mr. Hyde*
8. Lady Godiva
9. Becky Thatcher
10. All are science fiction writers.

Graduate Level

11. In what mountain area did Rip Van Winkle fall asleep?
12. Who was the main character in *The Hobbit*?
13. He wrote *Robinson Crusoe*.
14. In what story did Ichabod Crane's ride occur?

15. This was the famous sword of King Arthur.
16. He is known as the boy who did not wish to grow up.
17. He wrote *A Midsummer Night's Dream*.
18. Who wrote *Death of a Salesman*?
19. Alexander Selkirk's adventures inspired this book.
20. This poet wrote "Stopping by Woods on a Snowy Evening."

11. Catskills
12. Bilbo Baggins
13. Daniel Defoe
14. "The Legend of Sleepy Hollow"
15. Excalibur
16. Peter Pan
17. William Shakespeare
18. Arthur Miller
19. *Robinson Crusoe*
20. Robert Frost

Ph.D. Level

21. What was William Sydney's Porter's pen name?
22. Dr. Joseph Bell's life inspired this fictional character.
23. In this play the heroine's father spitefully kills her dog.

24. This hero of Sir Walter Scott's novels marries Rowena.
25. He wrote *The Three Musketeers*.
26. What was Samuel Clemens's pen name?
27. He wrote *War and Peace*.
28. Who is the hero of Goldsmith's comedy *She Stoops to Conquer*?
29. His poems include "The Rape of Lucrece."
30. This Russian won the Nobel Prize for Literature in 1958 but was forced to decline it.

21. O. Henry
22. Sherlock Holmes
23. *The Barretts of Wimpole Street*
24. Ivanhoe
25. Alexandre Dumas
26. Mark Twain
27. Leo Tolstoy
28. Young Marlow
29. William Shakespeare
30. Boris Pasternak

GENERAL: NUMBER TWO

Freshman Level

1. This book is remembered largely for its Yankee overseer, Simon Legree.
2. Who wrote *Love Story*?
3. He is the most translated English author.
4. She is the second most translated English author.
5. This book outlined a plan for political control of Germany.
6. He wrote *Shogun*.
7. He kept the most famous diary in the English language.
8. Author of *Animal Farm* and *1984*.
9. He wrote *Gulliver's Travels*.
10. *The Fountainhead* is about a man's struggle for success. What is his profession?

1. *Uncle Tom's Cabin*
2. Erich Segal
3. William Shakespeare
4. Agatha Christie
5. *Mein Kampf*
6. James Clavell
7. Samuel Pepys
8. George Orwell
9. Jonathan Swift
10. Architect

Graduate Level

11. This book explains how to obtain and keep political power.
12. This book was Harper Lee's only novel.
13. Herman Melville wrote this classic about a whale.
14. Why does Captain Ahab seek revenge on the whale?
15. This science fiction novel was written by Mary Shelley.
16. His masterpiece was *Ulysses*.
17. He wrote *The Blue Knight* and *The Choirboys*.
18. This book proposed the theory of evolution by means of natural selection.
19. This book claimed that control by capitalists would lead to a revolution and a classless society.
20. This novel by Ernest Hemingway won the Nobel Prize for Literature in 1954.

11. *The Prince*
12. *To Kill a Mockingbird*
13. *Moby Dick*
14. It cost him his leg.
15. *Frankenstein*
16. James Joyce
17. Joseph Wambaugh
18. *The Origin of Species*
19. *Das Kapital*
20. *The Old Man and the Sea*

Ph.D. Level

21. He wrote *The Scarlet Letter*.
22. What was the scarlet letter?
23. What did it stand for?
24. The movie *Apocalypse Now* was suggested by this British novel.
25. Who is the author of the book?
26. The 1901 novel *Kim* is set in India. Who wrote it?
27. What are used as chess pieces in *The Comedians*?
28. What is the captor of a piece expected to do?
29. In *The Little Prince* who teaches the prince what "to tame" means?
30. Who wrote *Fahrenheit 451*?

21. Nathaniel Hawthorne
22. *A*
23. Adultery
24. *Heart of Darkness*
25. Joseph Conrad
26. Rudyard Kipling
27. Miniature liquor bottles
28. Drink the contents
29. The fox
30. Ray Bradbury

CHARACTERS

Freshman Level

1. He went down the Mississippi with a slave named Jim.
2. She was determined to keep Tara plantation.
3. Unknowingly he killed his father and married his mother.
4. This sculptor fell in love with the statue of a woman.
5. This boy of good parentage was raised in a workhouse.
6. She was brutally murdered by Bill Sykes.
7. He fell in love with his own image.
8. This old Negro told humorous beast fables.
9. He is visited by ghosts on Christmas eve.
10. He was the captain of the *Nautilus*.

1. Huckleberry Finn
2. Scarlett O'Hara
3. Oedipus
4. Pygmalion
5. Oliver Twist
6. Nancy
7. Narcissus
8. Uncle Remus
9. Ebenezer Scrooge
10. Captain Nemo

Graduate Level

11. This released convict was pursued by Javert.
12. She is the narrator of the Arabian Nights stories.
13. He teaches the heroine to sing while she is in a trance.
14. He was the captain of the H.M.S. *Bounty*.
15. He roams for ten years before returning to Ithaca.
16. This simple but strong man dreams of a rabbit farm.
17. This Dickens character trains boys to steal for him.
18. His portrait grows old while he remains young-looking.
19. He bets he can pass off a Cockney flower girl as a lady.
20. He has memories of the many boys he taught at Brookfield.

11. Jean Valjean
12. Scheherazade
13. Svengali
14. William Bligh
15. Odysseus (Ulysses)
16. Lennie Small
17. Fagin
18. Dorian Gray
19. Henry Higgins
20. Mr. Chipping

Ph.D. Level

21. She and her goat, Djali, dance to earn a living.
22. He changed records in the Ministry of Truth.
23. He catches the biggest marlin ever brought into Havana.
24. She dislikes Fitzwilliam Darcy because of his pride.
25. He changes clothes with the Prince of Wales.
26. He is the detached, moody owner of Manderley.
27. As Augustus Caesar's wife, she poisons those who interfere with her plans for power.
28. This schoolteacher dreams of a marriage to Katrina.
29. He relates how he was kidnapped and flown to Shangri-La.
30. Through Louise he discovers the tragedy caused by Dr. Gordon's needless operations.

21. Esmeralda
22. Winston Smith
23. Santiago
24. Elizabeth Bennet
25. Tom Canty
26. Maximillian de Winter
27. Livia
28. Ichabod Crane
29. Hugh Conway
30. Parris Mitchell

AUTHORS
Name the authors of the works of literature.

Freshman Level

1. *Don Quixote*
2. *Pilgrim's Progress*
3. *Roots*
4. *Pygmalion*
5. *The Grapes of Wrath*
6. *A Doll's House*
7. *The Godfather*
8. *Gone With the Wind*
9. *Death of a Salesman*
10. *Alice's Adventures in Wonderland*

1. Miguel de Cervantes
2. John Bunyan
3. Alex Haley
4. George Bernard Shaw
5. John Steinbeck
6. Henrik Johan Ibsen
7. Mario Puzo
8. Margaret Mitchell
9. Arthur Miller
10. Lewis Carroll

Graduate Level

11. *The Lord of the Rings*
12. *The Catcher in the Rye*
13. *The Persian Boy*
14. *The Sun Also Rises*
15. *The Eagle Has Landed*
16. *Dr. Fu Manchu*
17. *The Hidden Persuaders*
18. *Sayonara*
19. *The Naked and the Dead*
20. *In Cold Blood*

11. J. R. R. Tolkien
12. J. D. Salinger
13. Mary Renault
14. Ernest Hemingway
15. Jack Higgins
16. Sax Rohmer
17. Vance Packard
18. James Michener
19. Norman Mailer
20. Truman Capote

Ph.D. Level

21. *Farewell My Lovely*
22. *The Martian Chronicle*
23. *The Midwich Cuckoos*
24. *Dr. Zhivago*
25. *Our Town*
26. *Long Day's Journey into Night*
27. *Women in Love*
28. *The Sound and the Fury*
29. *The Great Gatsby*
30. *Of Human Bondage*

21. Raymond Chandler
22. Ray Bradbury
23. John Wyndham
24. Boris Pasternak
25. Thornton Wilder
26. Eugene O'Neill
27. D. H. Lawrence
28. William Faulkner
29. F. Scott Fitzgerald
30. Somerset Maugham

BOOK TITLES-PULITZER PRIZE FOR FICTION
Complete the title.

Freshman Level

1.	1919	*The Magnificent . . .*	1.	*Ambersons*
2.	1928	*The Bridge of San Luis . . .*	2.	*Rey*
3.	1932	*The Good . . .*	3.	*Earth*
4.	1936	*Honey in the . . .*	4.	*Horn*
5.	1944	*Journey in the . . .*	5.	*Dark*
6.	1947	*All the King's . . .*	6.	*Men*
7.	1950	*The Way . . .*	7.	*West*
8.	1952	*The Caine . . .*	8.	*Mutiny*
9.	1958	*A Death in the . . .*	9.	*Family*
10.	1961	*To Kill a . . .*	10.	*Mockingbird*

Graduate Level

11.	1918	*His . . .*	11.	*Family*
12.	1921	*The Age of . . .*	12.	*Innocence*
13.	1923	*One of . . .*	13.	*Ours*
14.	1929	*Scarlet Sister . . .*	14.	*Mary*
15.	1930	*Laughing . . .*	15.	*Boy*
16.	1942	*In This Our . . .*	16.	*Life*
17.	1943	*Dragon's . . .*	17.	*Teeth*
18.	1945	*A Bell for . . .*	18.	*Adano*
19.	1948	*Tales of the South . . .*	19.	*Pacific*
20.	1949	*Guard of . . .*	20.	*Honor*

Ph.D. Level

21.	1962	*The Edge of . . .*	21.	*Sadness*
22.	1965	*The Keepers of the . . .*	22.	*House*
23.	1968	*The Confessions of Nat . . .*	23.	*Turner*
24.	1969	*House Made of . . .*	24.	*Dawn*
25.	1972	*Angle of . . .*	25.	*Repose*
26.	1973	*The Optimist's . . .*	26.	*Daughter*
27.	1975	*The Killer . . .*	27.	*Angels*
28.	1976	*Humboldt's . . .*	28.	*Gift*
29.	1978	*Elbow . . .*	29.	*Room*
30.	1979	*The Stories of John . . .*	30.	*Cheever*

CHARACTERS IN LITERATURE
Name the book in which the character appears.

Freshman Level

1. Tiny Tim
2. Quasimodo
3. Captain William Bligh
4. D'Artagnan
5. Becky Thatcher
6. Long John Silver
7. Tinker Bell
8. Scarlett O'Hara
9. Ichabod Crane
10. Simon Legree

1. *A Christmas Carol*
2. *The Hunchback of Notre Dame*
3. *Mutiny on the Bounty*
4. *The Three Musketeers*
5. *Tom Sawyer*
6. *Treasure Island*
7. *Peter Pan*
8. *Gone with the Wind*
9. "The Legend of Sleepy Hollow"
10. *Uncle Tom's Cabin*

Graduate Level

11. Sancho Panza
12. Chingachgook
13. Ishmael
14. Fagin
15. Tweedledum and Tweedledee
16. Heathcliff
17. Captain Nemo

18. Willy Loman
19. Madame Defarge
20. Pip

11. *Don Quixote*
12. *The Last of the Mohicans*
13. *Moby Dick*
14. *Oliver Twist*
15. *Through the Looking Glass*
16. *Wuthering Heights*
17. *Twenty Thousand Leagues Under the Sea*
18. *Death of a Salesman*
19. *A Tale of Two Cities*
20. *Great Expectations*

Ph. D. Level

21. Uriah Heep
22. Blanche DuBois
23. Tom Joad
24. David Balfour
25. Allan Quatermain
26. Parris Mitchell
27. Hugh Conway
28. Lennie Small
29. Jody Baxter
30. Tom Canty

21. *David Copperfield*
22. *A Streetcar Named Desire*
23. *The Grapes of Wrath*
24. *Kidnapped*
25. *King Solomon's Mines*
26. *King's Row*
27. *Lost Horizon*
28. *Of Mice and Men*
29. *The Yearling*
30. *The Prince and the Pauper*

PULITZER PRIZES IN LETTERS
Name the author. Provide the initials as a hint if necessary.

Freshman Level-Fiction

1.	1983	*The Color Purple*	A.W.	1.	Alice Walker
2.	1982	*Rabbit Is Rich*	J.U.	2.	John Updike
3.	1980	*The Executioner's Song*	N.M.	3.	Norman Mailer
4.	1976	*Humboldt's Gift*	S.B.	4.	Saul Bellow
5.	1961	*To Kill a Mockingbird*	H.L.	5.	Harper Lee
6.	1953	*The Old Man and the Sea*	E.H.	6.	Ernest Hemingway
7.	1952	*The Caine Mutiny*	H.W.	7.	Herman Wouk
8.	1940	*The Grapes of Wrath*	J.S.	8.	John Steinbeck
9.	1937	*Gone with the Wind*	M.M.	9.	Margaret Mitchell
10.	1932	*The Good Earth*	P.B.	10.	Pearl S. Buck

Graduate Level-Drama

11.	1940	*The Time of Your Life*	W.S.	11.	William Saroyan
12.	1943	*The Skin of Our Teeth*	T.W.	12.	Thornton Wilder
13.	1949	*Death of a Salesman*	A.M.	13.	Arthur Miller
14.	1955	*Cat on a Hot Tin Roof*	T.W.	14.	Tennessee Williams
15.	1957	*Long Day's Journey into Night*	E.O.	15.	Eugene O'Neill
16.	1967	*A Delicate Balance*	E.A.	16.	Edward Albee
17.	1973	*That Championship Season*	J.M.	17.	Jason Miller
18.	1979	*Buried Child*	S.S.	18.	Sam Shepard
19.	1981	*Crimes of the Heart*	B.H.	19.	Beth Henley
20.	1987	*Fences*	A.W.	20.	August Wilson

Ph. D. Level-Fiction

21.	1919	*The Magnificent Ambersons*	B.T.	21.	Booth Tarkington
22.	1926	*Arrowsmith*	S.L.	22.	Sinclair Lewis
23.	1928	*The Bridge of San Luis Rey*	T.W.	23.	Thornton Wilder
24.	1939	*The Yearling*	M.R.	24.	Marjorie K. Rawlings
25.	1943	*Dragon's Teeth*	U.S.	25.	Upton Sinclair
26.	1958	*A Death in the Family*	J.A.	26.	James Agee
27.	1960	*Advise and Consent*	A.D.	27.	Allen Drury
28.	1963	*The Reivers*	W.F.	28.	William Faulkner
20.	1984	*Ironweed*	W.K.	29.	William Kennedy
30.	1987	*A Summons to Memphis*	P.T.	30.	Peter Taylor

FANTASIES AND FAIRY TALES

Freshman Level

1. She lost a slipper.
2. He was Pinocchio's father.
3. He had the "Golden Touch."
4. He made a poor trade for his cow.
5. This girl's grandmother lived in the woods.
6. She pricked her finger on a spindle.
7. He sang "When You Wish Upon a Star."
8. His mother was killed by hunters.
9. They dropped bread crumbs so they wouldn't get lost.
10. This girl sat in a little chair and broke it.

1. Cinderella
2. Geppetto
3. King Midas
4. Jack
5. Red Riding Hood
6. Sleeping Beauty
7. Jiminy Cricket
8. Bambi
9. Hansel and Gretel
10. Goldilocks

Graduate Level

11. His big ears helped him to fly.
12. He was a super exterminator.
13. He thought nobody could guess his name.
14. He was the rabbit in the film *Bambi*.
15. He found a magic lamp.
16. He helped Santa on a foggy night.
17. He killed his wives.
18. He performed wonderful feats despite his small size.
19. He discovered the secret words "Open Sesame."
20. She fell down a rabbit's hole.

11. Dumbo
12. The Pied Piper
13. Rumpelstiltskin
14. Thumper
15. Aladdin
16. Rudolph
17. Bluebeard
18. Tom Thumb
19. Ali Baba
20. Alice

Ph.D. Level

21. He called his poor master the "Marquis of Carabas."
22. She let her hair down from a tower.
23. This lazy boy led Pinocchio to Toyland.
24. Thanks to his cat he became Lord Mayor of London.
25. When his beloved said "Yes," he became a prince.
26. He is always just one week old and can fly.
27. When Scrooge was young he worked for this man.
28. They wrote "Snow White and the Seven Dwarfs."
29. She was Peter Pan's fairy.
30. He was Rip Van Winkle's dog.

21. Puss in Boots
22. Rapunzel
23. Candlewick
24. Dick Whittington
25. The Beast
26. Peter Pan
27. Fezziwig
28. Brothers Grimm
29. Tinkerbell
30. Wolf

THE BIBLE

Freshman Level

1. He was Cain's brother.
2. He was the founder of the Jewish nation.
3. He was swallowed by a whale.
4. This is the City of David.
5. He was the "big fisherman."
6. He fought Goliath.
7. She cut Samson's hair.
8. He betrayed Jesus.
9. He was Jesus's human father.
10. This was the birthplace of Jesus.

1. Abel
2. Abraham
3. Jonah
4. Jerusalem
5. Peter
6. David
7. Delilah
8. Judas
9. Joseph
10. Bethlehem

Graduate

11. He is "the announcing angel."
12. He ordered every first-born son killed.
13. This is the chief river of Palestine.
14. This city was conquered by Joshua.
15. He was the Roman judge of Jesus.
16. This was the first of the ten plagues called down upon Egypt.
17. These scriptures reveal truth by divine agency.
18. God destroyed these wicked cities by fire.
19. The sacrament in which water initiates one into the Christian Church.
20. Goliath was a member of this tribe.

11. Gabriel
12. Herod
13. Jordan
14. Jericho
15. Pontius Pilate
16. Nile ran blood
17. *Revelations*
18. Sodom and Gomorrah
19. Baptism
20. Philistines

Ph.D. Level

21. The land on both sides of the Euphrates and between it and the Tigris was known as . . .
22. He was sold into Egypt and later promoted by the Pharaoh.
23. This first Christian martyr was stoned to death.
24. This was the site of Jesus's first miracle.
25. This is the second book of the Bible.
26. This is the supreme council of the Jewish nation.
27. Jesus lived here. It was one of the largest provinces of Palestine.
28. This was the land given to the Israelites by God.
29. He bought his twin brother Esau's birthright.
30. The tent of Jehovah which Moses was directed to erect in the wilderness was known as the . . .

21. Chaldea
22. Joseph
23. Stephen
24. Cana
25. *Exodus*
26. Sanhedrin
27. Galilee
28. Canaan
29. Jacob
30. Tabernacle

OCCUPATIONS
Name the occupation of each character. Try to answer without being told the title.

Freshman Level

1. Bob Cratchit	*A Christmas Carol*	1. Clerk for a merchant
2. The Artful Dodger	*Oliver Twist*	2. Child pickpocket
3. Rhett Butler	*Gone with the Wind*	3. Blockade runner
4. Sam Spade	*The Maltese Falcon*	4. Private detective
5. Henry Higgins	*Pygmalion*	5. Phonetics professor
6. Ichabod Crane	"The Legend of Sleepy Hollow"	6. Schoolmaster
7. Barbara	*Major Barbara*	7. Major in Salvation Army
8. Howard Roark	*The Fountainhead*	8. Architect
9. Catherine Barkley	*A Farewell to Arms*	9. Nurse
10. Tom Joad	*The Grapes of Wrath*	10. Farmer

Graduate Level

11. Atticus Finch	*To Kill a Mockingbird*	11. Lawyer
12. Yorick (when alive)	*Hamlet*	12. Jester
13. Wayne Hudson	*The Magnificent Obsession*	13. Brain surgeon
14. Parris Mitchell	*King's Row*	14. Physician in insane asylum
15. Torvald Helmer	*A Doll's House*	15. Bank manager
16. Uriah Heep	*David Copperfield*	16. Clerk to lawyer
17. John Wickliff Shawnessy	*Raintree County*	17. Teacher
18. Basil Hallward	*The Picture of Dorian Gray*	18. Artist
19. Winston Smith	*Nineteen Eighty-Four*	19. Changed records in the Ministry of Truth
20. Meg March	*Little Women*	20. Governess

Ph.D. Level

21. Widow Molloy	*The Matchmaker*	21. Ran a hat shop
22. Jake Barnes	*The Sun Also Rises*	22. Newspaper correspondent
23. Don Birnam	*The Lost Weekend*	23. Unsuccessful writer
24. Oliver Grant	*Look Homeward Angel*	24. Stonecutter
25. Sam Weller	*Pickwick Papers*	25. Valet (personal attendant)
26. Mr. Webb	*Our Town*	26. Editor-publisher of newspaper
27. Arthur Dimmesdale	*The Scarlet Letter*	27. Minister
28. Charles Strickland	*The Moon and Sixpence*	28. Stockbroker
29. Guy Pollock	*Main Street*	29. Lawyer
30. Per Hansa	*Giants in the Earth*	30. Farmer

SHAKESPEARIAN CHARACTERS

Freshman Level

1. She was driven mad by Hamlet.
2. She applies an asp to her bosom and dies.
3. This conspirator was a lean and ambitious person.
4. He plans to divide his kingdom among his daughters.
5. Prophecies, misunderstood, precede his defeat by Macduff.
6. This king was murdered by Macbeth.
7. He borrowed 3,000 ducats from Shylock.
8. He kills his wife, then executes himself when he learns of her innocence.
9. Unable to trust her nurse, she risks death to avoid a forced marriage.
10. Hamlet kills this king.

1. Ophelia
2. Cleopatra
3. Caius Cassius
4. King Lear
5. Macbeth
6. Duncan
7. Antonio
8. Othello

9. Juliet

10. Claudius

Graduate Level

11. This daughter of King Lear refuses to flatter him.
12. He is the mischievous sprite in *Midsummer Night's Dream*.

13. He was Romeo's father.
14. She was the shrew's pretty, younger sister.
15. He was more interested in his books of philosophy and magic than in affairs of state.
16. After being murdered by Macbeth's assassins, he appears at a ceremonial banquet.
17. She was Caesar's wife.
18. She tries to clean imaginary bloodstains from her hands.
19. He was Caesar's close friend.
20. He was the husband of the "shrew," Katharina.

11. Cordelia
12. Puck (Robin Goodfellow)
13. Montague
14. Bianca
15. Prospero

16. Banquo

17. Calpurnia
18. Lady Macbeth
19. Marc Antony
20. Petruchio

Ph.D. Level

21. He is separated from his twin sister during a shipwreck.
22. She was Celia's best friend and daughter of a duke.
23. He advises his companions to seek wisdom in the contemplation of feminine beauty.
24. He cannot obey his mother's injunction to betray himself in order to win the favor of the people.
25. He is one of the *Two Gentlemen of Verona*.
26. He refuses to look with sympathy upon Claudio's offence.
27. Falstaff sends an identical letter to two ladies. Name either of them.
28. She was raped by her husband's friend, Tarquin.
29. She wins Bertram as her husband through a trick.
30. This widow delivers a long curse near the beginning of the play.

21. Sebastian
22. Rosalind
23. Berowne

24. Coriolanus

25. Valentine or Proteus
26. Angelo
27. Mistress Page or Ford

28. Lucrece
29. Helena
30. Queen Margaret

POETRY

Finish the line of poetry.

Freshman Level

1. I will fear no evil; for thou art with me; thy rod and thy staff they . . .
2. All in the valley of death Rode the . . .
3. A jug of wine, a loaf of bread . . .
4. Dance like a butterfly, Sting like . . .
5. How do I love thee? Let me count . . .
6. Under the spreading chestnut tree The village smithy . . .
7. A thing of beauty is a . . .
8. Now of my threescore years and ten, Twenty will not . . .
9. I shot an arrow into the air, It fell to earth . . .
10. Jack Sprat could eat no fat, His wife could eat no lean, And so between them both, you see, They licked . . .

1. comfort me.
2. six hundred.
3. and thou.
4. a bee.
5. the ways.
6. stands.
7. joy forever.
8. come again.
9. I know not where.
10. the platter clean.

Graduate Level

11. A bunch of the boys were whooping it up in the Malamute . . .
12. A robin redbreast in a cage Puts all heaven . . .
13. Candy is dandy, But liquor . . .
14. I think that I shall never see A poem lovely as . . .
15. "The time has come," the Walrus said, "To talk . . .
16. By the shores of Gitche Gumee, By the shining . . .
17. The Owl and the Pussycat went to sea In a beautiful . . .
18. 'Twas the night before Christmas, when all through the house Not a creature was stirring —
19. Along the line of smoky hills, the crimson forest . . .
20. The woods are lovely, dark and deep. But I have promises to keep, And miles to go . . .

11. saloon.
12. in a rage.
13. is quicker.
14. a tree.
15. of many things."
16. Big-Sea-Water.
17. pea-green boat.
18. not even a mouse.
19. stands.
20. before I sleep.

Ph.D. Level

21. While I nodded, nearly napping, suddenly there came a tapping, As of some one gently rapping, rapping at my . . .
22. Oh, to be in England, now that . . .
23. When I set out for Lyonnesse, A hundred miles away, The rime was on the . . .
24. I never saw a Moor — I never saw the sea — Yet know I how the Heather looks And what a billow . . .
25. When I was a beggarly boy, And lived in a cellar damp, I had not a friend or a toy, But I had . . .
26. My name is Ozymandias, king of kings, Look on my works, ye mighty, . . .
27. I wandered lonely as a cloud That floats on high o'er vales and hills, When all at once I saw a crowd, A host of . . .
28. Loveliest of trees, the cherry now Is hung with bloom along . . .
29. Little Indian, Sioux or Crow, Little frosty Eskimo, Little Turk or Japanee, O! don't you wish that . . .
30. Whenever the moon and stars are set, Whenever the wind is high, All night long in the dark and wet, A man . . .

21. chamber door.
22. April's there.
23. spray.
24. be.
25. Aladdin's lamp.
26. and despair.
27. golden daffodils.
28. the bough.
29. you were me?
30. goes riding by.

LANGUAGE

PROVERBS

Freshman Level

1. The half is better than——
2. Give a man enough rope and——
3. Do not throw pearls——
4. The opera isn't over till——
5. One man's loss is——
6. Imitation is the sincerest——
7. The tree is known by——
8. You can have too much——
9. Many a true word——
10. There are two sides——

1. the whole.
2. he will hang himself.
3. before swine.
4. the fat lady sings.
5. another man's gain.
6. form of flattery.
7. its fruit.
8. of a good thing.
9. is spoken in jest.
10. to every question.

Graduate Level

11. The hand that rocks the cradle——
12. From the sublime to the ridiculous——
13. A watched pot——
14. It is a wise child that——
15. You cannot get blood——
16. A barking dog——
17. If you want peace you must——
18. Nothing is certain but——
19. The nearer the bone——
20. There's many a slip——

11. rules the world.
12. is only a step.
13. never boils.
14. knows its own father.
15. from a stone.
16. never bites.
17. prepare for war.
18. death and taxes.
19. the sweeter the meat.
20. 'twixt cup and lip.

Ph. D. Level

21. You cannot run with the hare——
22. When poverty comes in at the door——
23. Put your trust in God, and——
24. 'Tis better to have loved and lost——
25. Better to be an old man's darling than——
26. Believe nothing of what you hear——
27. He who rides a tiger——
28. A nod is as good as a wink to——
29. You never miss the water——
30. The mills of God grind slowly, yet they——

21. and hunt with the hounds.
22. love flies out of the window.
23. keep your powder dry.
24. than never to have loved at all.
25. a young man's slave.
26. and only half of what you see.
27. is afraid to dismount.
28. a blind horse.
29. till the well runs dry.
30. grind exceeding small.

THREESOMES
Provide the last word or words of the threesome.

1. Tom, Dick, and . . .
2. Stop, look, and . . .
3. Tall, dark, and . . .
4. Wine, women, and . . .
5. Hook, line, and . . .
6. Animal, vegetable, or . . .
7. Faith, hope, and . . .
8. Healthy, wealthy, and . . .
9. Sugar and spice and . . .
10. Readin', writin', and . . .

1. Harry
2. listen
3. handsome
4. song
5. sinker
6. mineral
7. charity
8. wise
9. everything nice
10. 'rithmetic

Graduate Level

11. Love, honor, and . . .
12. Hop, step, and . . .
13. Calm, cool, and . . .
14. Friends, Romans, . . .
15. Solids, liquids, and . . .
16. Huey, Dewey, and . . .
17. The Good, the Bad, and . . .
18. Lock, stock, and . . .
19. Larry, Curly, and . . .
20. Wynken, Blynken, and . . .

11. obey
12. jump
13. collected
14. Countrymen
15. gases
16. Louie
17. The Ugly
18. barrel
19. Moe
20. Nod

Ph.D. Level

21. Baubles, bangles, and . . .
22. Life, liberty, and . . .
23. Butcher, baker, and . . .
24. *Nina, Pinta*, and . . .
25. Father, Son, and . . .
26. Bell, book, and . . .
27. Flopsy, Mopsy, and . . .
28. Atchison, Topeka, & . . .
29. Maxene, Laverne, and . . .
30. Athos, Porthos, and . . .

21. beads
22. the pursuit of happiness
23. candlestick maker
24. *Santa Maria*
25. Holy Ghost
26. candle
27. Cottontail
28. Santa Fe
29. Patty
30. Aramis

DEFINITIONS

The speaker and his quotation are given; to what does the quotation refer? All answers are one word.

Freshman Level

1.	Karl Marx	"The opium of the people"	1. Religion
2.	George Meredith	"The last thing civilized by man"	2. Women
3.	Walter Landon	"Silent conversation"	3. Books
4.	O.K. Bovard	"Cow pasture pool"	4. Golf
5.	Oscar Wilde	"the name everyone gives to their mistakes"	5. Experience
6.	Voltaire	"an opinion without judgment"	6. Prejudice
7.	Charles Montesquieu	"the right to do what the laws allow"	7. Liberty
8.	Oscar Wilde	"the diary we all carry about with us"	8. Memory
9.	William Shakespeare	"the food of love"	9. Music
10.	Herbert Spencer	"organized knowledge"	10. Science

Graduate Level

11.	Henry Beecher	"the river of life in this world"	11. Love
12.	Herbert Spencer	"that which man is always trying to kill, but which ends up killing him"	12. Time
13.	William Shakespeare	"a stuff will not endure"	13. Youth
14.	Oliver Wendell Holmes	"what we pay for civilized society"	14. Taxes
15.	Ralph Waldo Emerson	"the first wealth"	15. Health
16.	Ernst Toller	"propaganda of the victors"	16. History
17.	Sir Thomas Browne	"the art of God"	17. Nature
18.	Ambrose Bierce	"a period of cheating between two periods of fighting"	18. Peace
19.	Juvenal	"the holiest of our gods"	19. Wealth
20.	Ambrose Bierce	"a ship big enough to carry two in fair weather but only one in foul."	20. Friendship

Ph. D. Level

21.	Will Durant	"the nucleus of civilization"	21. Family
22.	Joseph Joubert	"truth in action"	22. Justice
23.	Thomas Carlyle	"the dismal science"	23. Economics
24.	Robert Ingersoll	"places where pebbles are polished and diamonds are dimmed"	24. Colleges (schools)
25.	Henry Thoreau	"life near the bone"	25. Poverty
26.	Ambrose Bierce	"consisting of a master, a mistress, and two slaves, making in all two"	26. Marriage
27.	Ralph Waldo Emerson	"the archives of history"	27. Language
28.	Ralph Waldo Emerson	"a little fire, a little food, and an immense quiet"	28. Hospitality
29.	Matthew Arnold	"literature in a hurry"	29. Journalism
30.	Ralph Waldo Emerson	"the amassed thought and experience of innumberable minds"	30. Knowledge

PROVERBS
Complete each proverb.

Freshman Level

1. Beauty is only . . .
2. All roads lead to . . .
3. Don't make a mountain out of . . .
4. All that glitters . . .
5. Absence makes the heart . . .
6. All's fair in . . .
7. Let sleeping dogs . . .
8. A miss is as good as . . .
9. A new broom . . .
10. Learn to walk . . .

1. skin deep
2. Rome
3. a molehill
4. is not gold
5. grow fonder
6. love and war
7. lie
8. a mile
9. sweeps clean
10. before you run

Graduate Level

11. Honesty is . . .
12. Too many cooks . . .
13. Rome was not . . .
14. A rolling stone . . .
15. A stitch in time . . .
16. It's no use crying . . .
17. One good turn . . .
18. Out of sight . . .
19. If a thing is worth doing . . .
20. Where there's life . . .

11. the best policy
12. spoil the broth
13. built in a day
14. gathers no moss
15. saves nine
16. over spilt milk
17. deserves another
18. out of mind
19. it is worth doing well
20. there's hope

Ph.D. Level

21. Strike while . . .
22. The wish is father . . .
23. The road to hell is paved with . . .
24. The spirit is willing but . . .
25. One swallow doesn't . . .
26. Many hands . . .
27. Necessity is . . .
28. Time and tide . . .
29. Still waters . . .
30. Fine feathers make . . .

21. the iron is hot
22. to the thought
23. good intentions
24. the flesh is weak
25. make a summer
26. make light work
27. the mother of invention
28. wait for no man
29. run deep
30. fine birds

"MAC WORDS"
All answers start with the letters "mac."

Freshman Level

1. A Shakespearean tragedy.
2. A club-shaped staff used as a symbol of authority.
3. The first Prime Minister of Canada.
4. A mountainous region in southeastern Europe.
5. The longest river in Canada.
6. A large heavy knife with a blade shaped like a broadsword.
7. Tube-shaped pasta.
8. A leading American general of World War II.
9. Trade name for a chemical solution that temporarily incapacitates the victim when sprayed in the face.
10. A valuable food fish related to the tuna.

1. Macbeth
2. Mace
3. MacDonald, John A.
4. Macedonia
5. Mackenzie
6. Machete
7. Macaroni
8. MacArthur, Douglas
9. Mace
10. Mackerel

Graduate Level

11. An overseas province of Portugal on the coast of China.
12. His name stands for all that is cunning and two-faced in statesmanship.
13. A waterproof outer garment was invented by him.
14. One of the greatest managers in baseball history.
15. He became Prime Minister of England in 1957.
16. A fringe lace or trimming of knotted thread.
17. A type of coat or boat or blanket.
18. Exaggeratedly masculine.
19. To pave with small stones.
20. The site of an ancient Inca city.

11. Macao
12. Machiavelli
13. Macintosh, Charles
14. Mack, Connie
15. Macmillan, Harold
16. Macrame
17. Mackinaw
18. Macho (machismo)
19. Macadamize
20. Machu Picchu

Ph.D. Level

21. A measure of speed.
22. A straight line over a vowel to indicate the long form.
23. A small cookie made of ground almonds.
24. An historical line of Jewish rulers.
25. A long-tailed parrot of South America.
26. Gruesome or ghastly.
27. The whole universe.
28. A large smooth shiny seed that is eaten as a nut.
29. A city in Georgia.
30. An island in northern Michigan.

21. Mach
22. Macron
23. Macaroon
24. Maccabees
25. Macaw
26. Macabre
27. Macrocosm
28. Macadamia nut
29. Macon
30. Mackinac

"AZ" WORDS
Use the clue to find the word containing the combination "az."

Freshman Level

1. A shaving utensil.
2. Hitler's men.
3. Sky blue.
4. A public square.
5. Astonish.
6. A large country in South America.
7. Mythical female warriors.
8. Mexican Indians.
9. A labyrinth.
10. Unwilling to work.

1. Razor
2. Nazis
3. Azure
4. Plaza
5. Amaze
6. Brazil
7. Amazons
8. Aztecs
9. Maze
10. Lazy

Graduate Level

11. An antitank weapon.
12. A marketplace in the east.
13. A fad.
14. A yellow sapphire.
15. To bewilder or stun.
16. To demolish as a building.
17. A large flame.
18. A danger.
19. A glassy finish on a surface.
20. A sports jacket.

11. Bazooka
12. Bazaar
13. Craze
14. Topaz
15. Daze
16. Raze
17. Blaze
18. Hazard
19. Glaze
20. Blazer

Ph.D. Level

21. A small tree of the birch family.
22. Stun with brilliance.
23. A grill.
24. Adorn magnificiently.
25. Christ raised him from the dead.
26. To heckle or deride.
27. A mosaic type of flooring.
28. A Polish folkdance.
29. A flower.
30. Cattle do this.

21. Hazel
22. Bedazzle
23. Brazier
24. Emblazon
25. Lazarus
26. Razz
27. Terrazzo
28. Mazurka
29. Azalea
30. Graze

NAMES OF THINGS: GENERAL
What is the thingamajig called?

Freshman Level

1. The narrowest part of an hourglass.		1. Waist
2. The center of a head of lettuce.		2. Heart
3. The indentations on a golf ball.		3. Dimples
4. The vertical part of a stairstep.		4. Riser
5. The prime hitting area on a tennis racket.		5. Sweet spot
6. Mustard, ketchup, relish, and onions.		6. Condiments
7. A bowl-shaped utensil having perforations, used as a strainer.		7. Colander
8. A wheel, free to swivel, used to support furniture.		8. Caster
9. A brimless hat with a flat crown and usually a tassel, worn by men in Turkey.		9. Fez
10. The mallet used by a court judge.		10. Gavel

Graduate Level

11. The rope used for hoisting and lowering a flag.		11. Halyard
12. The unsmoked tobacco in the bottom of a pipe bowl.		12. Dottle
13. The vertical posts supporting a stair bannister.		13. Balusters
14. The weight at the end of a pendulum.		14. Bob
15. A piece of burning wood.		15. Firebrand
16. A small mug shaped like a man with a cocked hat.		16. Toby
17. The rhythm instrument held in the hand by dancers and clicked together during the dance.		17. Castanets
18. A basin, often on a pedestal, used for baptisms.		18. Font
19. An iron hook with a handle for lifting fish.		19. Gaff
20. The vertical panel on the lower part of a desk which conceals the person's lower body.		20. Modesty panel

Ph.D. Level

21. The curved front part of a toboggan.		21. Hood
22. The part of a key that you hold.		22. Bow
23. The pointed prong found on some candlesticks on which a candle is impaled.		23. Pricket
24. The space between adjacent teeth of a saw.		24. Gullet
25. The ceiling cap that covers the junction box for hanging lighting fixtures.		25. Canopy
26. The smoke from a pipe.		26. Lunt
27. Each of the four straight sections of a paper clip.		27. Leg
28. The metal wire device securing corks on bottles of true champagne.		28. Coiffe
29. The piece protruding out the top end of an umbrella.		29. Ferrule
30. The soft portion beneath the crust of a loaf of bread.		30. Crumb

NAMES OF THINGS: CLOTHING
What is the thingamajig called?

Freshman Level

1.	The short skirt worn by female ballet dancers.	1. Tutu
2.	The loose-fitting outer robe worn by Romans.	2. Toga
3.	A sweater that opens the full length of the center front.	3. Cardigan
4.	The garment worn by Hindu women.	4. Sari
5.	The bearskin hat worn by British guardsmen.	5. Busby
6.	The ornamental fringed shoulder pad on a uniform.	6. Epaulet
7.	The leather leggings without a seat worn by cowboys.	7. Chaps
8.	A band for the head worn by women on formal occasions.	8. Tiara
9.	A hoodlike knitted cap covering the head and neck.	9. Balaclava
10.	The proper name for a watch pocket.	10. Fob

Graduate Level

11.	A dress hanging straight from the shoulders.	11. Chemise
12.	Cloth formed into a skirt by being wrapped around the body, worn chiefly by Malays.	12. Sarong
13.	A small skullcap worn by schoolboys.	13. Beanie
14.	Glittering pieces of metal used on clothing for decoration.	14. Sequins
15.	The loop on a belt that holds the loose end.	15. Keeper
16.	A woman's undergarment top worn to camouflage a brassiere.	16. Camisole
17.	The slit in the back panel of a man's suit jacket.	17. Vent
18.	A shoe or house slipper that doesn't grip the heel.	18. Mule
19.	An outdoor garment for infants consisting of a large envelope with an attached hood.	19. Bunting
20.	A low shoe, without laces, gripping the foot chiefly at the toe and heel.	20. Pump

Ph.D. Level

21.	Leg covering from ankle to knee, consisting of a narrow band of cloth wrapped spirally.	21. Puttee
22.	The kerchieflike Arab headdress.	22. Kaffiyeh
23.	The cord that Arabs use to hold down the headdress.	23. Agal
24.	The long, loose hooded cloak worn by Arabs.	24. Burnous
25.	The indentations at the front of a fedora.	25. Pinch
26.	An Eskimo-type boot with a soft leather sole.	26. Mukluk
27.	The slit in a garment, forming the opening.	27. Placket
28.	The proper name for a Jewish skullcap.	28. Yarmulke
29.	The proper name for a Jewish prayer shawl.	29. Tallith
30.	The close-fitting cloth, usually white, worn by nuns to cover the throat and the sides of the face.	30. Wimple

COLORFUL EXPRESSIONS

Give an expression, containing the given color, which means the same as the given clue.

Freshman Level

1. Black: illegal system of selling goods.
2. Blue: an aristocrat.
3. White: small untruth.
4. Red: excessive procedures and paperwork.
5. Pink: healthy.
6. White: office worker.
7. Red: caught with the goods.
8. Blue: very infrequently.
9. Green: be able to grow things well.
10. Blue: be depressed.

1. Black market
2. A blue blood
3. White lie
4. Red tape
5. In the pink
6. White-collar worker
7. Caught red-handed
8. Once in a blue moon
9. Have a green thumb
10. Have the blues or feel blue

Graduate Level

11. Red: treated royally.
12. Black: refuse to accept one into a group.
13. White: make someone appear faultless.
14. Black: prohibit telecasting of a program in a given area.
15. Green: area set aside for nature.
16. Red: in a deficit position.
17. Black: bad one in a family.
18. Red: very special day.
19. Blue: very loyal.
20. Black: in print.

11. Red-carpet treatment
12. Blackball
13. Whitewash
14. Blackout
15. Greenbelt
16. In the red
17. Black sheep
18. Red-letter day
19. True blue
20. In black and white

Ph.D. Level

21. Silver: eloquent.
22. White: something too expensive to maintain.
23. Red: diversion intended to distract from the issue.
24. Gold: evade assigned work.
25. Blue: unexpectedly.
26. Silver: wealth
27. Red: live it up.
28. Green: inexperienced person.
29. Yellow: coward.
30. Green: waiting room for show-business performers.

21. Silver-tongued
22. White elephant
23. Red herring
24. Goldbrick
25. Out of the blue
26. Silver spoon
27. Paint the town red
28. Greenhorn
29. Yellow belly
30. Green room

DRINKING TERMS

Freshman Level

1. A Japanese liquor fermented from rice
2. Straight-up means without . . .
3. The finest of the brandies is known as . . .
4. Glasses are placed on these to avoid marring furniture.
5. A Russian liquor made from potatoes
6. The sauce added to enhance a Bloody Mary
7. A brandy glass with a rounded bowl is a brandy . . .
8. How many ounces in a jigger?
9. This red syrup used in cocktails is made from the pulp of pomegranates.
10. What might be described as "foxy"?

1. Sake
2. Ice
3. Cognac
4. Coasters
5. Vodka
6. Tabasco
7. Snifter
8. 1½ ounces
9. Grenadine
10. Wine (flavor)

Graduate Level

11. What does VSO mean?
12. This favorite Viking drink was derived from honey.
13. How many ounces is a pony?
14. What type of peel compliments a Pimm's no. 1 cup?
15. This liquor is distilled from fermented molasses or cane juice.
16. Beers containing few hops are called . . .
17. The finished fragrance of wine in the glass is its . . .
18. The dregs of wine or beer are called . . .
19. Retsina wine is identified with which country?
20. VSOP means . . . ?

11. Very special old
12. Mead
13. 1 ounce
14. Cucumber peel
15. Rum
16. Lagers
17. Bouquet
18. Lees
19. Greece
20. Very special old pale

Ph.D. Level

21. The cage holding a champagne cork in place
22. What is fob?
23. The concave area at the bottom of some wine bottles is a . . .
24. A muddler is more commonly called a . . .
25. The largest champagne bottle is a . . .
26. The empty space in a bottle between the liquid and the top is . . .
27. BIB is an acronym for . . .
28. The streaks that run down the side of a glass after wine has been swirled in it are . . .
29. If the label has the letters DOM on it the bottle contains . . .

30. The metal foil covering the top of a wine bottle

21. Agrafe or *coiffe*
22. Froth on beer
23. Punt or kick
24. Swizzle stick
25. Nebuchadnezzar
26. Ullage
27. Bottled in bond
28. Legs
29. Benedictine (The initials stand for *Deo Optimo Maximo*, "to God, the best and greatest")
30. Capsule

FAMILIAR QUESTIONS

Fill in the blank with a single word to complete the familiar question.
A few answers require a name consisting of more than one word.

Freshman Level

1. Is there a doctor in the . . .?
2. Brother, can you spare a . . .?
3. Is everybody . . .?
4. They shoot . . ., don't they?
5. How much is that . . . in the window?
6. Am I my brother's . . .?
7. Why did the chicken cross the . . .?
8. Wherefore art thou, . . .?
9. What is this thing called . . .?
10. Baa, baa, black sheep, have you any . . .?

1. house
2. dime
3. happy
4. horses
5. doggie
6. keeper
7. road
8. Romeo
9. love
10. wool

Graduate Level

11. What's in a . . .?
12. Are you sleeping, ...?
13. Do you know the muffin man that lives in . . . . . .?
14. Who killed . . . . . .?
15. Et tu, . . .?
16. What kind of . . . am I?
17. I wonder who's . . . her now?
18. How are things in . . .?
19. How do I . . . thee?
20. Do you know the way to . . . . . .?

11. name
12. Brother John
13. Drury Lane
14. Cock Robin
15. Brute
16. fool
17. kissing
18. Gloccamora
19. love
20. San José

Ph.D. Level

21. Do you think the rain will hurt the . . .?
22. Is Paris . . .?
23. Death, where is thy . . .
24. What is so rare as a day in . . .?
25. Where have all the . . . gone?
26. Pardon me boy, is that the . . . .?
27. Where are the . . . of yesteryear?
28. What hath God . . .?
29. . . . . . . , won't you please come home?
30. Do I hear a . . .?

21. rhubarb
22. burning
23. sting
24. June
25. flowers
26. Chattanooga Choo Choo
27. snows
28. wrought
29. Bill Bailey
30. waltz

SPANISH
Translate into English.

Freshman Level

1. Hombre		1. Man	
2. Señor		2. Mr.	
3. Rio		3. River	
4. Loco		4. Crazy	
5. Tierra		5. Earth	
6. Cinco		6. Five	
7. Mucho		7. Much	
8. Adios		8. Good-bye	
9. Muchacha		9. Girl	
10. Diablo		10. Devil	

Graduate Level

11. Mañana		11. Tomorrow	
12. Buenos dias		12. Good morning	
13. Por favor		13. Please	
14. Alto! (command)		14. Stop!	
15. Buenas noches		15. Good night (evening)	
16. No fumar		16. No smoking	
17. Mar		17. Sea	
18. Sur		18. South	
19. Billete		19. Ticket	
20. Reserva		20. Reservation	

Ph.D. Level

21. Diez		21. Ten	
22. Salida		22. Departure	
23. Hoy		23. Today	
24. No entiendo		24. I do not understand	
25. Sexto		25. Sixth	
26. Un poco		26. A little	
27. Habla usted ingles?		27. Do you speak English?	
28. Cuánto vale?		28. What does it cost?	
29. Casa Blanca		29. White House	
30. Primera clase		30. First class	

HASH-HOUSE SLANG
Provide the meaning of the diner slang—e.g. Drown a hen. *Answer:* chicken soup.

Freshman Level Beverages and desserts

1. Moo juice
2. Brown cow
3. On the house / tin roof / Adam's ale.
4. Bucket of mud
5. Shake in the hay
6. Houseboat / banshee
7. Van midget
8. Cold spot
9. Tall one
10. Draw one

1. Milk
2. Chocolate milk
3. Water
4. Dish of chocolate ice cream
5. Strawberry milkshake
6. Banana split
7. Small vanilla milkshake
8. Iced tea
9. Beer
10. Cup of coffee

Graduate Level General instructions

11. Burn it
12. On the hoof
13. High and dry
14. Paint it red
15. Smear /grease /salve
16. All the way / through the garden
17. Let it walk
18. Hold the hail
19. Bridge
20. Crowd

11. Well done
12. Very rare
13. Without trimmings (condiments)
14. With ketchup
15. Butter
16. With all the trimmings
17. To go (to be taken out)
18. Without ice
19. Four of anything
20. Three of anything

Ph.D. Level Breakfast and sandwiches

21. BLT
22. Pig between sheets
23. Cowboy
24. Two high
25. Adam and Eve on a raft
26. Birdseed
27. Wreck a pair
28. Noah's boy on whiskey
29. You too (U-2)
30. Eve's a traitor

21. Bacon, lettuce, and tomato sandwich
22. Ham on white bread
23. Western omelet
24. Toast
25. Two poached eggs on toast
26. Cold cereal
27. Scrambled eggs
28. Ham on rye
29. Submarine sandwich
30. Eggs Benedict

OCCUPATIONS

Fill in the blank with the name of an occupation.

Freshman Level

1. Death of a . . . .
2. Too many . . . spoil the broth.
3. An apple a day keeps the . . . away.
4. The . . . in the dell.
5. Shoes of the . . . .
6. The absent-minded . . . .
7. An apple for the . . . .
8. The . . . of Seville.
9. Old . . . never die.
10. The . . . and I.

1. Salesman
2. Cooks
3. Doctor
4. Farmer
5. Fisherman
6. Professor
7. Teacher
8. Barber
9. Soldiers
10. King

Graduate Level

11. To Catch a . . . .
12. Diary of a Mad . . . .
13. Only her . . . knows for sure.
14. Butcher, . . ., candlestick maker.
15. What do you do with a drunken . . . ?
16. I'm a ramblin' wreck from Georgia Tech and a heck of an . . . .
17. My compliments to the . . . .
18. Rich man, poor man, . . . man, thief.
19. The Deer . . . .
20. The . . . Who Came in from the Cold.

11. Thief
12. Housewife
13. Hairdresser
14. Baker
15. Sailor
16. Engineer
17. Chef
18. Beggar
19. Hunter
20. Spy

Ph.D. Level

21. Tinker, . . ., soldier, sailor.
22. Midnight . . . .
23. The . . . in the Rye.
24. The . . . of Venice.
25. The List of Adrian . . . .
26. The . . . Rebellion.
27. The . . . of Wakefield.
28. The Walrus and the . . . .
29. Here come de . . . .
30. The Hoodlum . . . .

21. Tailor
22. Cowboy
23. Catcher
24. Merchant
25. Messenger
26. Boxer
27. Vicar
28. Carpenter
29. Judge
30. Priest

GEOGRAPHY

THE UNITED STATES: GENERAL

Freshman Level

1. The U.S. capital is Washington, D.C. What does D.C. mean?
2. In which city was President Kennedy killed?
3. In what state is Chicago?
4. Name the major mountain chain in the eastern states.
5. Which state is directly north of Oregon?
6. In which state is Hollywood?
7. Which state capital has the same name as the state?
8. Name the most northeasterly of the 48 contiguous states.
9. Which city is second largest in population?
10. In which state is Las Vegas?

1. District of Columbia
2. Dallas
3. Illinois
4. Appalachian
5. Washington
6. California
7. Oklahoma City
8. Maine
9. Chicago
10. Nevada

Graduate Level

11. Name the highest mountain in the United States.
12. There is a North and South Dakota. Name another similar pair of states.
13. Name the most southerly state.
14. Name a state starting with the letter G.
15. Near what city is Alcatraz located?
16. How many states border the Pacific Ocean?
17. Which state is smallest in size?
18. What state begins and ends with the letter O?
19. Name another state with only four letters.
20. Name the northernmost state.

11. Mount McKinley
12. North and South Carolina
13. Hawaii
14. Georgia
15. San Francisco
16. Five
17. Rhode Island
18. Ohio
19. Utah or Iowa
20. Alaska

Ph.D. Level

21. In which state is the Grand Coulee Dam?
22. Where is the Alamo?
23. What is the official name of Rhode Island?

24. Which state is divided into two parts by a large lake?
25. Name the large city at the west end of Lake Superior.
26. On what mountain are four presidents' faces carved?
27. Which state was named for Queen Elizabeth I?

28. Name the lowest point in the United States.
29. Where is the baseball hall of fame?
30. Four states meet at one point. Three of them are Arizona, New Mexico, and Utah. Name the fourth.

21. Washington
22. San Antonio, Texas
23. Rhode Island and Providence Plantations
24. Michigan
25. Duluth
26. Mount Rushmore
27. Virginia (for the Virgin Queen)
28. Death Valley, California
29. Cooperstown, New York
30. Colorado

SOUTH OF THE BORDER
Name the country that is to the south of the given country.

Freshman Level

1. Canada
2. Switzerland
3. Denmark
4. U.S.A.
5. Lebanon
6. Venezuela
7. France
8. Nepal
9. United Kingdom
10. Mongolia

1. U.S.A.
2. Italy
3. West Germany
4. Mexico
5. Israel
6. Brazil
7. Spain
8. India
9. France
10. China

Graduate Level

11. Iraq
12. Mexico
13. Poland
14. Ecuador
15. Bulgaria
16. Afghanistan
17. Guyana
18. Egypt
19. Syria
20. Paraguay

11. Saudi Arabia
12. Guatemala
13. Czechoslovakia
14. Peru
15. Greece/Turkey
16. Pakistan
17. Brazil
18. Sudan
19. Jordan
20. Argentina

Ph. D. Level

21. Malaysia
22. Nicaragua
23. Romania
24. Laos
25. Angola

26. Botswana
27. Albania
28. Honduras
29. Luxembourg
30. Hungary

21. Indonesia
22. Costa Rica
23. Bulgaria
24. Cambodia
25. Namibia (Southwest Africa)
26. South Africa
27. Greece
28. Nicaragua
29. France
30. Yugoslavia

Europe: General

Freshman Level

1. The Acropolis is located in this city.
2. This is Germany's most famous university town.
3. This Irish town, famed in song, is a long way from Dublin
4. This is Switzerland's "banking town."
5. Luxembourg is surrounded by West Germany, France, and . . .
6. Italy and Yugoslavia are separated by this sea.
7. This strait separates Spain and Morocco.
8. The Virgin Mary appeared here. It is now a Portuguese shrine.
9. This country consists of .73 square miles of apartment buildings, clubs, cliffs, and coastline.
10. The best-known Oktoberfest is held here.

1. Athens
2. Heidelberg.
3. Tipperary
4. Zurich
5. Belgium
6. Adriatic
7. Gibraltar
8. Fatima
9. Monaco
10. Munich

Graduate Level

11. Johann Strauss honored this river in music.
12. This Austrian city was the site of the 1964 and 1976 Winter Olympics.
13. This Hungarian city is divided into two sections by the Danube River.
14. This peninsula is connected to the main body of Greece by the Isthmus of Corinth.
15. This country, which is on the Adriatic Sea, borders on both Greece and Yugoslavia.
16. This is the site of a famous Greek oracle.
17. The most famous system of archaeological excavations lies here.
18. This sea is surrounded by the U.S.S.R., Turkey, Bulgaria, and Rumania.
19. This sea lies between Greece and Italy.
20. This country offers Dracula Tours.

11. Danube
12. Innsbruck
13. Buda/Pest
14. Peloponnesus
15. Albania
16. Delphi
17. Pompeii
18. Black Sea
19. Ionian Sea.
20. Rumania

Ph.D. Level

21. Lake Balaton, the largest unbroken stretch of inland water in central Europe, is in this country.
22. The "running of the bulls" is held in this Spanish city.
23. This is one of Denmark's main industrial towns. Hans Christian Anderson was born here.
24. George Bernard Shaw once referred to this Yugoslavian city as "the pearl of the Adriatic, a paradise on earth."
25. Pentland Firth separates these islands on Scotland's north coast.
26. You'll find the ruined temple of Zeus and Hera here.
27. This is Europe's most westerly country.
28. The most westerly point of land in England is known as . . .
29. The chief rivers of this country are Vistula, Oder, Bug, Warta, and Narew.
30. This country's anthem is "Yes, We Love This Land of Ours."

21. Hungary
22. Pamplona
23. Odense
24. Dubrovnik
25. Orkney Islands
26. Olympia
27. Iceland
28. Land's End
29. Poland
30. Norway

THE UNITED STATES: STATE CAPITALS

Give the capital city of each state named.

Freshman Level

1. Georgia		1. Atlanta
2. Massachusetts		2. Boston
3. New York		3. Albany
4. Tennessee		4. Nashville
5. Texas		5. Austin
6. Utah		6. Salt Lake City
7. Virginia		7. Richmond
8. Rhode Island		8. Providence
9. Ohio		9. Columbus
10. Mississippi		10. Jackson

Graduate Level

11. Florida		11. Tallahassee
12. Hawaii		12. Honolulu
13. Alaska		13. Juneau
14. Arizona		14. Phoenix
15. California		15. Sacramento
16. Colorado		16. Denver
17. Idaho		17. Boise
18. Kansas		18. Topeka
19. Maine		19. Augusta
20. Maryland		20. Annapolis

Ph.D. Level

21. Minnesota		21. Saint Paul
22. Michigan		22. Lansing
23. Nebraska		23. Lincoln
24. New Mexico		24. Santa Fe
25. Nevada		25. Carson City
26. Pennsylvania		26. Harrisburg
27. Wyoming		27. Cheyenne
28. Wisconsin		28. Madison
29. Washington		29. Olympia
30. West Virginia		30. Charleston

THE UNITED STATES: LARGE CITIES
Name the city from its location.

Freshman Level

1. At east end of Lake Erie, on the Niagara River.
2. On lower west shore of Lake Michigan.
3. At mouth of the Hudson River.
4. On Massachusetts Bay, at the mouth of the Charles and Mystic rivers.
5. Between Virginia and Maryland, on the Potomac River.
6. In northeastern Texas, on Trinity River.
7. In west Texas, on Rio Grande.
8. In southern Florida, on Biscayne Bay.
9. In southwestern Tennessee, on the Mississippi River.
10. On Lake St. Clair.

1. Buffalo
2. Chicago
3. New York
4. Boston
5. Washington, D.C.
6. Dallas
7. El Paso
8. Miami
9. Memphis
10. Detroit

Graduate Level

11. In eastern Nebraska, on the Missouri River.
12. At the beginning of the Ohio River, in Pennsylvania.
13. In southwestern Ohio, on the Ohio River.
14. At the junction of the Missouri and Kansas rivers.
15. On St. Johns River, 20 miles from the Atlantic Ocean.
16. On Lake Erie at the mouth of the Cuyahoga River.
17. On the Patapsco River, about 12 miles from Chesapeake Bay.
18. In Washington, on Puget Sound.
19. In southeastern Texas, near the Gulf of Mexico.
20. Fifty miles from San Francisco, on south San Francisco Bay.

11. Omaha
12. Pittsburgh
13. Cincinnati
14. Kansas City
15. Jacksonville
16. Cleveland
17. Baltimore
18. Seattle
19. Houston
20. San Jose

Ph.D. Level

21. In Indiana, on the West Fork of the White River.
22. In Pennsylvania, at the beginning of the Ohio River.
23. At the junction of the Schuylkill and Delaware rivers.
24. On Maumee River at Lake Erie
25. In the north central part of Kentucky, on the Ohio River.
26. On the east side of San Francisco Bay.
27. Between the Mississippi River and Lake Ponchartrain.
28. On the Elizabeth River and Hampton Roads.
29. On the North Canadian River.
30. In southeastern Arizona, on the Santa Cruz River.

21. Indianapolis
22. Pittsburgh
23. Philadelphia
24. Toledo
25. Louisville
26. Oakland
27. New Orleans
28. Norfolk
29. Oklahoma City
30. Tucson

ORIGINS OF STATE NAMES
All answers are state names.

Freshman Level

1. In honor of the first president of the country.
2. In honor of George II of England.
3. In honor of Louis XIV of France.
4. From an Indian word meaning Father of Waters.
5. From a English county.
6. From the country to the south of the United States.
7. In honor of Sir William Penn.
8. From the French meaning "green mountain."
9. In honor of Elizabeth, Virgin Queen of England.
10. Meaning "land of Indians."

1. Washington
2. Georgia
3. Louisiana
4. Mississippi
5. New Hampshire
6. New Mexico
7. Pennsylvania
8. Vermont
9. Virginia, West Virginia
10. Indiana

Graduate Level

11. From the Spanish meaning "feast of flowers."
12. In honor of Henrietta Marie (Queen of Charles I).
13. First used to distinguish the mainland from the offshore islands.
14. In honor of the English Duke of York.
15. In honor of Charles I of England.
16. From one of the English Channel Islands.
17. From the Greek island of the same name.
18. From the Spanish meaning "mountain."
19. From an Indian word meaning "great river."
20. Means Gem of the Mountains.

11. Florida
12. Maryland
13. Maine
14. New York
15. North/South Carolina
16. New Jersey
17. Rhode Island
18. Montana
19. Ohio
20. Idaho

Ph. D. Level

21. From the Spanish for "snowcapped."
22. From an Indian word meaning "great lake."
23. From an Indian word meaning "beside the long tidal river."
24. From the Spanish "ruddy" or "red."
25. From an Indian word meaning, "mountains and valleys alternating."
26. From a tribe name meaning "people of the mountains."
27. From an Indian word meaning "friends."
28. From an Indian word meaning "great land" or "mainland."
29. From an Indian word meaning "little spring."
30. From an imaginary island in a Spanish book.

21. Nevada
22. Michigan
23. Connecticut
24. Colorado
25. Wyoming
26. Utah
27. Texas
28. Alaska
29. Arizona
30. California

THE UNITED KINGDOM

Freshman Level

1. This Scottish site is famous for its monster.
2. The United Kingdom consists of England, Scotland, Northern Ireland, and . . .
3. The mystery of this ancient circle of stones has never been completely solved.
4. This is one of the Queen's residences and is the largest inhabited castle in the world.
5. This is England's oldest university.
6. This area was the home of Robin Hood's merry band.
7. This is the national anthem.
8. This is the name given to the flag.
9. This is the capital city of Wales.
10. This is the capital of Scotland.

1. Loch Ness
2. Wales
3. Stonehenge
4. Windsor Castle
5. Oxford
6. Sherwood Forest
7. "God Save the Queen"
8. Union Jack
9. Cardiff
10. Edinburgh

Graduate Level

11. This is the capital of Northern Ireland.
12. Famed in song, the loch is one of Scotland's great scenic attractions.
13. Thomas Becket was murdered here in 1170.
14. William Shakespeare was born and died here.
15. This London street houses the majority of England's national newspaper offices.
16. This is actually the name of the bell, not the clock tower itself.
17. This is the largest island in the United Kingdom.
18. This is the second largest city in the United Kingdom.
19. These Scottish islands are famous for their ponies.
20. Jersey and Guernsey are islands in this group.

11. Belfast
12. Loch Lomond
13. Canterbury Cathedral
14. Stratford-upon-Avon
15. Fleet Street
16. Big Ben
17. Great Britain
18. Birmingham
19. Shetland Islands
20. The Channel Islands

Ph.D. Level

21. This language is used on official occasions on the Isle of Man.
22. These two island groups form the northernmost part of the British Isles.
23. Chaucer wrote a literary tale about pilgrims journeying to this medieval city.
24. The capital of this island in the Irish Sea is Douglas.
25. To which island group do these islands belong: Skye, Mull, Lewis, and Harris?
26. This is England's most famous botanical gardens.
27. This thriving seaport is on the River Mersey.
28. This is the highest mountain peak in the United Kingdom.
29. This is the longest river in the United Kingdom.
30. The Strait of Dover is the narrowest point of the English Channel. How wide is it? (Correct if within 3 miles)

21. Manx
22. Orkney Islands, Shetland Islands
23. Canterbury
24. Isle of Man
25. The Hebrides
26. Kew Gardens
27. Liverpool
28. Ben Nevis
29. Severn
30. 21 miles

THE UNITED STATES: CITY NICKNAMES

Name the city identified with each nickname.

Freshman Level

1.	Big D	1.	Dallas, Tex.
2.	Beantown	2.	Boston, Mass.
3.	Big Apple	3.	New York, N.Y.
4.	City of Brotherly Love	4.	Philadelphia, Pa.
5.	Film Capital of the World	5.	Hollywood, Calif.
6.	Twin Cities	6.	Minneapolis – St. Paul, Minn.
7.	Motown	7.	Detroit, Mich.
8.	Mile High City	8.	Denver, Colo.
9.	Biggest Little City in the World	9.	Reno, Nev.
10.	Windy City	10.	Chicago, Ill.

Graduate Level

11.	Steel City	11.	Pittsburgh, Pa.
12.	Chocolate Capital of the World	12.	Hershey, Pa.
13.	Bison City	13.	Buffalo, N.Y.
14.	Birthplace of American Liberty	14.	Lexington, Mass.
15.	Pittsburgh of the South	15.	Birmingham, Ala.
16.	Insurance City	16.	Hartford, Conn.
17.	Glass Capital of the World	17.	Toledo, Ohio
18.	Gateway to the West	18.	St. Louis, Mo.
19.	Gulf City	19.	Mobile, Ala.
20.	Rubber Capital of the World	20.	Akron, Ohio

Ph.D. Level

21.	Orchid City	21.	Hilo, Hawaii
22.	Peanut City	22.	Suffolk, Va.
23.	Silk City	23.	Paterson, N.J.
24.	Cement City	24.	Allentown, Pa.
25.	Canoe City	25.	Old Town, Me.
26.	Railroad City	26.	Indianapolis, Ind.
27.	Pretzel City	27.	Reading, Pa.
28.	Crescent City	28.	New Orleans, La.
29.	Palmetto City	29.	Charleston, S.C.
30.	Celery City	30.	Kalamazoo, Mich.

LANDMARKS

Freshman Level

1. This is the most famous French landmark.
2. Until 1970 this New York landmark was the world's tallest inhabited structure.
3. This American landmark is called the Rock.
4. This is the main attraction in Anaheim, California.
5. Name the most famous landmark in Pisa, Italy.
6. This landmark consists of 840 acres in the center of Manhattan Island.
7. British monarchs are crowned here.
8. Twelve avenues radiate from this colossal monument in Paris.
9. In which city is the Grand Canal?
10. This landmark is the largest single ancient structure.

1. Eiffel Tower
2. Empire State Building
3. Alcatraz Island
4. Disneyland
5. The Leaning Tower
6. Central Park
7. Westminster Abbey
8. Arc de Triomphe
9. Venice
10. Great Wall of China

Graduate Level

11. Stone pillars in concentric circles are found at this famous English site.
12. This London landmark was Sir Christopher Wren's masterpiece.
13. In which American city is Basin Street?
14. World's tallest building is in Chicago. Name it.
15. Romans built this famous wall across Britain.
16. Name Rio de Janeiro's most famous mountain.
17. Name the tallest structure in Washington, D.C.
18. Name San Antonio's famous historical landmark.
19. Headquarters of London's Metropolitan Police is known as . . .
20. Name the most famous landmark in Agra, India.

11. Stonehenge
12. St. Paul's Cathedral
13. New Orleans
14. The Sears Tower
15. Hadrian's Wall
16. Sugar Loaf
17. Washington Monument
18. The Alamo
19. New Scotland Yard
20. Taj Mahal

Ph.D. Level

21. *Maid of the Mist* is usually found near this landmark.
22. Name the most famous falls in Africa.
23. Swallows are said to fly back to this California mission village.
24. This London square commemorates the defeat of the French fleet in 1805.
25. This is Hawaii's most famous beach.
26. In what city is Tivoli Gardens?
27. Name London's most famous waxworks museum.
28. New York Philharmonic played in this building on West 57th Street.
29. Toronto's most visible landmark is . . .

30. Large statue named Christ the Redeemer overlooks this South American city.

21. Niagara Falls
22. Victoria Falls
23. San Juan Capistrano
24. Trafalgar Square
25. Waikiki
26. Copenhagen
27. Madame Tussaud's
28. Carnegie Hall
29. The CN (Canadian National) Tower
30. Rio de Janeiro

CITIES : SITES

Name the city in which each site is located

Freshman Level

1. Red Square
2. The Acropolis
3. The Alamo
4. Champs-Elysées
5. Nelson's Monument
6. Trevi Fountain
7. Wall Street
8. Liberty Bell
9. Guggenheim Museum
10. Wailing Wall

1. Moscow
2. Athens
3. San Antonio
4. Paris
5. London
6. Rome
7. New York
8. Philadelphia
9. New York
10. Jerusalem

Graduate Level

11. Drury Lane
12. Sugarloaf Mountain
13. Tidal Basin
14. Grand Canal
15. Nob Hill
16. Arch of Titus
17. Loop
18. Little Mermaid
19. Petit Trianon
20. Copacabana Beach

11. London
12. Rio de Janeiro
13. Washington
14. Venice
15. San Francisco
16. Rome
17. Chicago
18. Denmark
19. Versailles
20. Rio de Janeiro

Ph.D. Level

21. Summer Palace
22. Savile Row
23. Bridge of Sighs
24. Hearst Castle
25. Baseball Hall of Fame
26. Plaka
27. Rialto Bridge
28. Spanish Steps
29. Tivoli Gardens
30. Arch of Hadrian

21. Peking
22. London
23. Venice
24. San Simeon, California
25. Cooperstown, New York
26. Athens
27. Venice
28. Rome
29. Copenhagen
30. Athens

ROME

Freshman Level

1. How many hills was Rome originally built on?
2. This state is the center of the Roman Catholic Church.
3. This river runs through Rome.
4. Rome is sometimes known by this name.
5. Who was the first Emperor of Rome?
6. This dictator modernized Rome
7. Funeral services for deceased popes are held here.
8. Michelangelo designed the dome of this great basilica.
9. This well-known ancient building is four-storied and oval in shape.
10. These are underground chambers where the early Christians were buried.

1. Seven
2. Vatican City
3. Tiber
4. The Eternal City
5. Augustus
6. Benito Mussolini
7. Sistine Chapel
8. St. Peter's
9. The Colosseum
10. Catacombs

Graduate Level

11. This building was built as a mausoleum, later became a prison, and today is a museum.
12. An open place where public meetings were held was called a ...
13. The chief street of ancient Rome was the Via Sacra, meaning ...
14. This was the best known of the Roman temples.
15. The square or plaza in front of St. Peter's is the ...
16. What shape is the ground plan of St. Peter's?
17. These twin sons were the legendary founders of Rome.
18. Ancient Rome had many elaborate *thermae*. What were they?
19. Michelangelo completed this picture on the end wall of the Sistine Chapel in 1541.
20. St. Peter's was built over a crypt believed to contain whose body?

11. Castel Saint Angelo (Hadrian's Tomb)
12. Forum
13. Sacred Way
14. Pantheon
15. Piazza San Pietro
16. Cruciform
17. Romulus, Remus
18. Public baths.
19. Last Judgment
20. Saint Peter's

Ph.D. Level

21. This great paved highway led from Rome's gates to Capua, eventually to Brundisium (Brindisi).
22. Most of the palaces of the early wealthy Romans were built on this hill.
23. This modern work of art is a colossal monument, which towers over the central square of the city.
24. What are these: Barberini, Borghese, Farnese, and Orsini?
25. Who designed the huge open area in front of St. Peter's enclosing the plaza in a circular colonnade?
26. What was established by the Treaty of Lateran?
27. What are the soldiers of Vatican City known as?
28. Rome lies about seventeen miles from this sea.
29. Name one of the two hills which start with the letter C.
30. The Codex Vaticanus is located in the Vatican Library. What is it?

21. Appian Way
22. Palatine Hill
23. Monument to King Emmanuel II
24. Private palaces
25. Giovanni Bernini
26. Vatican City
27. Swiss Guards
28. Tyrrhenian Sea
29. Caelian, Capitoline
30. One of three early translations of Old Testament

NORTH AMERICA

Freshman Level

1. What U.S. state borders on two oceans?
2. The largest fresh-water lake in North America (and the world).
3. The highest mountain in North America.

4. Give in order the three largest American states in area.

5. What North American country has the greatest crude oil reserves?
6. Give two American states that contain a woman's name in theirs.
7. Name the largest state east of the Mississippi.
8. What state of the U.S.A. borders on one and only one other state?
9. The most populous city in North America.
10. What American state has the lowest population?

1. Alaska
2. Lake Superior
3. Mount McKinley, Alaska
4. Alaska, Texas, California
5. Mexico

6. Maryland, Virginia, West Virginia
7. Georgia
8. Maine

9. Mexico City
10. Alaska

Graduate Level

11. Name the largest island on North America's east coast (not Greenland).
12. Name the largest island on the west coast.
13. Name the largest of the Hawaiian Islands.
14. How many American states border on the Pacific Ocean?
15. Name the most southerly North American country.
16. Florida is bounded on the north by these two states.
17. Name the two large peninsulas of Mexico.

18. How many territories make up Canada's Northwest Territories?
19. What Canadian province borders on no other province?
20. Name the four American states bordering on Mexico.

11. Newfoundland

12. Vancouver Island
13. Hawaii
14. Five
15. Panama
16. Georgia, Alabama
17. Yucatan, Baja California

18. One

19. Prince Edward Island
20. Texas, California, Arizona, New Mexico.

Ph.D. Level

21. Name the largest Mexican town on the U.S. border.
22. What state of the U.S.A. ranks fourth in area?
23. Name the American state that borders on eight other states.
24. Name one of the three states having boundaries formed only by straight lines.
25. The only state whose boundaries have no straight lines.
26. Name the largest country in Central America in area.
27. The U.S.A. has fifty states. How many states are there in Mexico?
28. Name the largest American state that doesn't border on a foreign country.
29. The Mexican state with the same name as a breed of dog.
30. What two countries border Mexico to the south?

21. Tijuana
22. Montana
23. Tennessee
24. Colorado, Utah, Wyoming

25. Hawaii
26. Nicaragua
27. Thirty-one

28. Nevada

29. Chihuahua
30. Guatemala, Belize

STRUCTURES: PAST AND PRESENT

Give the city where each structure is located.

Freshman Level

1.	Eiffel Tower	1.	Paris
2.	Parthenon	2.	Athens
3.	The Statue of Liberty	3.	New York City
4.	Golden Gate Bridge	4.	San Francisco
5.	Empire State Building	5.	New York City
6.	The Kremlin	6.	Moscow
7.	The Louvre	7.	Paris
8.	The Coliseum	8.	Rome
9.	Westminster Abbey	9.	London
10.	Rockefeller Center	10.	New York City

Graduate Level

11.	Saint Sophia	11.	Istanbul
12.	The Taj Mahal	12.	Agra
13.	Saint Paul's Cathedral	13.	London
14.	The Astrodome	14.	Houston
15.	The Hanging Gardens	15.	Babylon
16.	The Sears Tower	16.	Chicago
17.	The Great Mosque and Kaaba	17.	Mecca
18.	The Bosporus Bridge	18.	Istanbul
19.	Saint Mark's Cathedral	19.	Venice
20.	The Superdome	20.	New Orleans

Ph.D. Level

21.	The Alhambra	21.	Granada
22.	The Pyramids	22.	Gizeh
23.	The Dome of the Rock	23.	Jerusalem
24.	Circus, Circus	24.	Las Vegas
25.	The Temple of Artemis	25.	Ephesus
26.	The Colossus	26.	Rhodes
27.	The Pentagon	27.	Arlington, Va.
28.	The Gateway Arch	28.	Saint Louis, Mo.
29.	The Statue of Zeus	29.	Olympia, Greece
30.	The C.N. Tower	30.	Toronto

STATES: HAWAII, TEXAS, AND ALASKA

Freshman Level (All questions concern Hawaii)

1. The largest Hawaiian Island is . . .
2. Hawaiians use this word to welcome you.
3. The largest mountain in the islands is . . .

4. This is the capital city of Hawaii.
5. Name Hawaii's most famous volcano.
6. Hawaii is the world's largest producer of this fruit.
7. This is Honolulu's most famous beach.
8. Name the island Honolulu is located on.
9. What is a Hawaiian floral garland called?
10. A Hawaiian feast is called a . . .

1. Hawaii
2. Aloha
3. Mauna Kea (White Mountain)
4. Honolulu
5. Diamond Head
6. Pineapple
7. Waikiki
8. Oahu
9. Lei
10. Luau

Graduate Level (All questions concern Texas)

11. Which states are more populous than Texas?
12. What is the state capital?
13. What is the largest city in Texas?
14. This river forms part of the state's southern border.
15. Four states border on Texas. Two are Arkansas and New Mexico. Name the other two.
16. This city's twin city is Juarez, Mexico.
17. What river forms part of the northern border of Texas?
18. What are these: Texoma, Amistad, and Falcon?
19. This city is considered to be the banking and insurance capital of the Southwest.
20. This city's attractions include the Tower of the Americas and the Alamo.

11. New York, California
12. Austin
13. Houston
14. Rio Grande
15. Louisiana, Oklahoma
16. El Paso
17. Red River
18. Lakes
19. Dallas
20. San Antonio

Ph.D. Level (All questions concern Alaska)

21. This is the capital city of Alaska.
22. This is the largest city.
23. This Alaskan peak is the highest in North America.
24. This river flows through the heart of Alaska's interior.
25. This sea is west of Alaska.
26. These islands are off Alaska's southwest coast.
27. This is Alaska's largest interior city.
28. This city was the site of 20,000 prospectors in the early 1900's.
29. Spectacular oil strikes have been made in this bay. off the North Slope.
30. What are these: Illamna, Becharof, and Tustumena?

21. Juneau
22. Anchorage
23. Mount McKinley
24. Yukon River
25. Bering Sea
26. Aleutian Islands
27. Fairbanks
28. Nome
29. Prudhoe Bay
30. Lakes

ISLANDS

Freshman Level

1. New Zealand consists of two islands. Name them.
2. The largest island in the world.
3. General MacArthur vowed to return to these islands.
4. The Nationalist Chinese occupy this island.
5. The boroughs of Queens and Brooklyn are on this island.
6. This Mediterranean island was a British garrison during World War II.
7. Portuguese islands far out in the Atlantic.
8. Aruba and Curaçao are controlled by what country?
9. This Canadian island is the world's fifth largest.
10. The world's second largest island is located north of Australia. It is . . .

1. North Island, South Island
2. Greenland
3. Philippines
4. Taiwan (Formosa)
5. Long Island
6. Malta
7. Azores
8. The Netherlands
9. Baffin Island
10. New Guinea

Graduate Level

11. The large island off the east coast of southern Africa.
12. The island on which England is located.
13. In which ocean or sea are the Seychelles?
14. Zanzibar is part of what country?
15. The mutinous crew of the *Bounty* went to this island.
16. The largest of the Hawaiian islands.
17. This Pacific island's puzzling monoliths attract ethnologists.
18. The largest of the Greek islands.
19. This island is a state of Australia.
20. The city of Palermo is on this island.

11. Madagascar
12. Britain
13. Indian Ocean
14. Tanzania
15. Pitcairn
16. Hawaii
17. Easter Island
18. Crete
19. Tasmania
20. Sicily

Ph.D. Level

21. This island forms part of Nova Scotia.
22. This island is in the mouth of the Saint Lawrence River.
23. Amchitka is one of the islands in this U.S. island group.
24. Guadalcanal is a member of this island group.
25. Devon, Melville, and Southhampton islands belong to what country?
26. This Caribbean island hosted the 1979 Pan American Games.
27. Guernsey, Jersey, and Sark are the three major islands in this group.
28. This island group is off the east coast of southern South America.
29. In which ocean or sea are the Balearic Islands?
30. The islands of Luzon and Mindanao are part of what country?

21. Cape Breton
22. Anticosti Island
23. Aleutian Islands
24. Solomon Islands
25. Canada
26. Puerto Rico
27. Channel Islands
28. Falkland Islands
29. Mediterranean Sea
30. Philippines

WASHINGTON, D.C.

Freshman Level

1. Who selected the site for Washington, D.C.?

2. On what river is the city located?
3. The President lives in this building.
4. What do the initials D.C. stand for?
5. Washington stands on territory that once belonged to this state.
6. Headquarters of the Defense Department.
7. What is the tallest structure in Washington?
8. Here you can view *The Spirit of St. Louis* and the *Flyer*.
9. What is the address of the White House?

10. What computerized system opened in Washington in 1976?

1. Commissioners appointed by George Washington
2. Potomac
3. The White House
4. District of Columbia
5. Maryland
6. The Pentagon
7. Washington Monument
8. The Smithsonian
9. 1600 Pennsylvania Avenue
10. Subway system

Graduate Level

11. This site houses the Congress, the Supreme Court, and the Library of Congress.
12. This popular world-exploration magazine has its headquarters in Washington.
13. This is considered to be the largest library in the United States.
14. Which cemetery is across the river from Washington proper?
15. In what year was the District of Columbia established?
16. This fashionable area was designated a national monument in 1967?
17. This center boasts fine performances in opera, dance, music, and theater.
18. Name Washington's oldest university.
19. The oldest building in Washington. (Cornerstone laid in 1792.)
20. This annual festival is held sometime between mid-March and mid-April.

11. Capitol Hill
12. *National Geographic*
13. Library of Congress
14. Arlington National
15. 1790
16. Georgetown

17. John F. Kennedy Center

18. Georgetown University
19. The White House
20. Cherry Blossom Festival

Ph.D. Level

21. Lafayette Square in front of the White House is dominated by the equestrian statue of whom?
22. This is located at the corner of First and East Capitol Streets.
23. What are these: Anacostia and Rock Creek?
24. Name two of the three major airports serving Washington, D.C.

25. What was Major Pierre Charles L'Enfant's contribution?
26. In which building is the Declaration of Independence housed?
27. What is Blair House?
28. This circular stone structure stands on the south shore of the Tidal Basin in West Potomac Park.
29. This building encloses a large statue of a president in meditation, sitting on a large armchair.
30. The District of Columbia was originally a square area. What were the dimensions?

21. Andrew Jackson

22. Supreme Court

23. Parks
24. National, Dulles, Baltimore-Washington
25. Designed the city.
26. The National Archives
27. President's guest house
28. Thomas Jefferson Memorial
29. Lincoln Memorial

30. Ten miles by ten miles

CANADA

Freshman Level

1. How many provinces are there in Canada?
2. What are the other land areas called?
3. What is the largest province in size?
4. Name the most westerly province.
5. Name the most easterly province.
6. What province extends farthest south?
7. What is the nation's capital?
8. What is the longest river?
9. What is the mainland part of Newfoundland called?
10. Name the three Prairie Provinces.

1. Ten
2. Territories
3. Quebec
4. British Columbia
5. Newfoundland
6. Ontario
7. Ottawa
8. Mackenzie River
9. Labrador
10. Alberta, Manitoba, Saskatchewan

Graduate Level

11. What are the two territories called?
12. Who followed Pierre Trudeau as prime minister?
13. What is the smallest province?
14. What province has a name which is Latin for "New Scotland?"
15. Name Canada's largest bay.
16. This city is known as the Honeymoon Capital of the World.
17. These Scandinavian warriors landed in Canada about 1000 A.D.
18. What does CPR stand for?
19. How does Canada rank in size among the countries in the world?
20. What province has Fredericton as its capital city?

11. Yukon, Northwest
12. Brian Mulroney
13. Prince Edward Island
14. Nova Scotia
15. Hudson Bay
16. Niagara Falls, Ontario
17. Vikings
18. Canadian Pacific Railway
19. Second (after the U.S.S.R.)
20. New Brunswick

Ph.D. Level

21. What river is Montreal located on?
22. Name the two main federal political parties.
23. What is the highest mountain?
24. This B.C. valley is noted for its apples.
25. The largest lake totally within Canada.
26. What does NDP stand for?
27. When is Thanksgiving celebrated in Canada?
28. This bay separates Nova Scotia and New Brunswick.
29. This parallel forms a large part of the southern border.
30. Canada's largest island.

21. St. Lawrence
22. Conservatives, Liberals
23. Mount Logan, Y.T.
24. Okanagan, B.C.
25. Great Bear Lake, N.T.
26. New Democratic Party
27. Second Monday in October
28. Bay of Fundy
29. 49th
30. Baffin Island

PLACES AND LOCATIONS: REAL AND/OR IMAGINARY

Freshman Level

1. This city is sacred to Jews, Christians, and Muslims.
2. This was the birthplace of Mohammed.
3. This was the home of King Arthur.
4. This is known as the "lost continent."
5. This utopian city was said to be in Tibet.
6. The buildings here are the best examples of classical symmetry and elegant beauty.
7. The Pillars of Hercules were located here.
8. Davy Crockett and Jim Bowie were killed here.
9. The souls of slain Norse heroes went here.
10. This desert is located in southeast California.

1. Jerusalem
2. Mecca
3. Camelot
4. Atlantis
5. Shangri-La
6. Acropolis, Athens

7. Gibraltar
8. The Alamo, Texas
9. Valhalla
10. Mojave Desert

Graduate Level

11. Evidence of buried treasure was found on this Canadian island in 1795.
12. Stone pillars in concentric circles are found here.
13. This legendary city was known as the "City of Gold."
14. The legendary island to which King Arthur was taken after his final battle.
15. Three peasant children witnessed visions here in 1917.
16. A large bronze statue of Helios (Apollo) was located here.
17. Large underwater blocks are found off this Bahamian island.
18. The home of the Hobbits in Tolkien's Middle-Earth.
19. The site of a famous healing shrine in France.
20. A territory in Canada noted for a gold rush.

11. Oak Island, N.S.
12. Stonehenge, England
13. El Dorado
14. Avalon
15. Fatima, Portugal
16. Rhodes
17. Bimini
18. The Shire
19. Lourdes
20. The Yukon

Ph.D. Level

21. From the air, huge geometric figures can be seen here.
22. These caves contain paintings 15,000 – 20,000 years old.
23. This is known as "the Lost City of the Incas."
24. The Temple of Artemis (Diana) was located here.
25. The Lost Dutchman gold mine is said to be located here.
26. This now-abandoned city was the largest in the world in the year 1000.
27. This Buddhist fortress was known as the "Forbidden City."
28. In 1590, sailors bringing supplies found the colonists here had vanished. The only clue was the word "Croatan" carved on a tree.
29. This was the setting for *Tom Sawyer*.
30. This holy city on the Ganges river attracts pilgrims.

21. Nazca, Peru
22. Lascaux Caves, France
23. Macchu Pichu, Peru
24. Ephesus, Turkey
25. Superstition Mts., Ariz.
26. Angkor, Cambodia
27. Lhasa, Tibet
28. Roanoke Island, S.C.

29. Hannibal, Mo.
30. Varanasi (Benares), India

HISTORY

MYTHS AND LEGENDS

Freshman Level

1. King Arthur kept court here.
2. She was the Greek goddess of beauty.
3. This horned horse could be captured only by a virgin.
4. This island lay beyond the Gates of Hercules.
5. The name "Thursday" is derived from this Nordic god.
6. Everything he touched turned to gold.
7. This was King Arthur's sword.
8. Ponce de Leon sought this key to eternal life.
9. He performed twelve great labors.
10. Hers was the face that launched a thousand ships.

1. Camelot
2. Aphrodite
3. Unicorn
4. Atlantis
5. Thor
6. King Midas
7. Excalibur
8. Fountain of Youth
9. Hercules
10. Helen of Troy

Graduate Level

11. This was a fabulous winged horse.
12. The Greek hero Jason sought this.
13. To look upon her meant turning to stone.
14. This bird was reborn from its own ashes.
15. He was king of the Norse gods.
16. He was the Roman god of the sea.
17. The knights of the Round Table sought this.
18. He was the Roman equivalent of Zeus.
19. These were a nation of warlike women.
20. You crossed this river to enter Hades.

11. Pegasus
12. Golden Fleece
13. Medusa
14. Phoenix
15. Odin
16. Neptune
17. Holy Grail
18. Jupiter
19. Amazons
20. Styx

Ph.D. Level

21. He was Sir Lancelot's son.
22. This king led the Greeks in the Trojan War.
23. This appeared in the night sky when the Valkyrie rode forth.
24. He gave fire to mortals.
25. He flew too close to the sun.
26. He was King Arthur's son.
27. This island was Ulysses' home.
28. The twelve most illustrious knights of Charlemagne were called . . .
29. These two brothers were suckled by a she-wolf.
30. She opened a box releasing Vice, Plague, Spite, and so on.

21. Sir Galahad
22. Agamemnon
23. Northern Lights
24. Prometheus
25. Icarus
26. Mordred
27. Ithaca
28. Peers or paladins
29. Romulus and Remus
30. Pandora

V-J DAY

Freshman Level

1. What do the letters V-J stand for?
2. What was the date of V-J day?
3. On August 6 an atomic bomb was dropped on this city.
4. This president made the decision to drop the bomb.
5. What type of plane carried the bomb?
6. Who was the Emperor of Japan at the time?
7. On August 9 a second bomb was dropped on this city.
8. Also on August 9 the U.S.S.R. began hostilities against Japan by invading——.
9. Name the project that produced the atomic bomb.
10. Who headed the project?

1. Victory over Japan
2. September 2, 1945
3. Hiroshima
4. Harry Truman
5. B-29 (Superfortress)
6. Hirohito
7. Nagasaki
8. Manchukuo (Manchuria)
9. Manhattan Project
10. Robert Oppenheimer

Graduate Level

11. Where did the Japanese sign the terms of surrender?
12. Who signed on behalf of the Allies?

13. Where was the battleship at the time?
14. On March 16 this tiny island was captured, placing the Allies' planes within 750 miles of Tokyo.
15. The next island to fall was about 350 miles from Japan. It was——.
16. In a desperate attempt to stem the tide, these suicide pilots were used.
17. Translate the word "Kamikaze."
18. In this proclamation of July 26 the Allied Powers called for "unconditional surrender."
19. On August 10 Japan agreed to surrender but made this sole condition.
20. The Allies replied that the Emperor's fate would be decided by the——.

11. Battleship *Missouri*
12. Gen. Douglas MacArthur
13. Tokyo harbor
14. Iwo Jima
15. Okinawa
16. Kamikaze
17. Divine Wind
18. Potsdam Proclamation
19. Emperor remain as sovereign ruler.
20. Japanese people

Ph. D. Level

21. The atomic bomb had been successfully tested at this site.

22. What was the name of the plane that dropped the bomb?
23. What was the Hiroshima bomb nicknamed?
24. What was the Nagasaki bomb nicknamed?
25. What role did Paul Tibbets, Jr., play in the victory?
26. The point on the ground directly above or below the point of detonation is called——.
27. The planned invasion of the Japanese home islands in November was given this code name.
28. How was the news of the surrender given to the Japanese people?
29. The only Axis head of government to be hanged by the Allies was——.
30. The U.S. officially ended its war with Japan on April 28, 19——.

21. Alamogordo, New Mexico
22. *Enola Gay*
23. Little Boy
24. Fat Man
25. Piloted the *Enola Gay*
26. Ground Zero
27. Operation Olympic
28. Emperor on radio
29. Hideki Tojo
30. 1952

THE UNITED STATES: PRESIDENTS

Freshman Level

1. He killed President Lincoln.
2. Roosevelt led Rough Riders up San Juan Hill here.
3. The only president a state was named for.
4. President Lincoln was killed in this building.
5. Texas governor who was wounded when John F. Kennedy was killed.
6. This president dismissed General MacArthur.
7. Alaska and Hawaii became states under this president.
8. His presidential retreat was San Clemente.
9. His presidential retreat was Hyannis Port.
10. He killed President Kennedy.

1. John Wilkes Booth
2. Cuba
3. George Washington
4. Ford's Theater
5. John Connally
6. Harry S Truman
7. Dwight D. Eisenhower
8. Richard Nixon
9. John F. Kennedy
10. Lee Harvey Oswald

Graduate Level

11. President Ford's vice-president.
12. President Johnson's vice-president.
13. This president won a Pulitzer Prize.
14. He walked softly but carried a big stick.
15. He was known as Old Hickory.
16. The title of President Kennedy's best-known book.
17. Two sons of this president died in World War II.
18. Abraham Lincoln debated with this man in 1858.
19. The only president to die before both of his parents.
20. The first First Lady to be received privately by the Pope.

11. Nelson Rockefeller
12. Hubert Humphrey
13. John F. Kennedy
14. Theodore Roosevelt
15. Andrew Jackson
16. *Profiles in Courage*
17. Theodore Roosevelt
18. Stephen Douglas
19. John F. Kennedy
20. Jacqueline Kennedy

Ph.D. Level

21. Presidents Madison, Monroe, Polk, Buchanan, Garfield and Carter have this in common.
22. This president's mother, Nancy Hanks, was illegitimate.
23. Code name for the hotline between Moscow and Washington.
24. Mt. Washington, Mt. Adams, Mt. Monroe, Mt. Jefferson, Mt. Pierce, and Mt. Jackson are located in this range.
25. President Kennedy's last words.
26. The minimum age of a U.S. president.
27. Name of the scandal during Harding's administration involving naval oil reserve leases.
28. President responsible for the Louisiana Purchase.
29. Eisenhower's grandson is this man's son-in-law.
30. The only vice-president elected to the presidency years after his vice-presidential term.

21. First name James
22. Abraham Lincoln
23. Molink
24. White Mountains, New Hampshire
25. "My God, I've been hit."
26. 35 years old
27. Teapot Dome
28. Thomas Jefferson
29. Richard Nixon
30. Richard Nixon

MEDIEVAL HISTORY

Freshman Level

1. This is another name for the bubonic plague.
2. He was crowned emperor of the Holy Roman Empire in 800.
3. He founded the order of Franciscan friars.
4. These campaigns were waged to win back the Holy Land.
5. He was probably the first European to reach North America.
6. She led the French army that lifted the seige at Orleans.
7. He founded Islam in the seventh century A.D.
8. The Eastern Roman Empire was superseded by this empire.
9. The Vikings believed that warriors who fell in battle went here.
10. King Richard I of England is also known by this name.

1. The Black Death
2. Charlemagne
3. St. Francis of Assisi
4. The Crusades
5. Leif Ericson
6. Joan of Arc
7. Muhammad
8. Byzantine Empire
9. Valhalla
10. Richard the Lion Hearted

Graduate Level

11. Contests between two knights were known as . . .
12. He united the Mongol tribes and waged wars from Korea to Bulgaria.
13. This Spanish hero of Castile fought under both Spanish and Moorish flags.
14. In 1215 King John put his seal to this charter of liberties.
15. William the Conqueror defeated Harold here in 1066.
16. The houses of Lancaster and York fought each other in these conflicts.
17. Marco Polo lived at the court of this emperor of China.
18. The Normans introduced this form of land distribution to England.
19. When the English kings laid claim to the French crown, it led to this conflict.
20. In this campaign 50,000 children were sent to win back the Holy Land.

11. Jousts
12. Genghiz Khan
13. El Cid
14. Magna Carta
15. Battle of Hastings
16. Wars of the Roses
17. Kublai Khan
18. Feudal system
19. Hundred Years' War
20. Children's Crusade

Ph.D. Level

21. This king of the Franks founded the Carolingian Dynasty.
22. This Mongol warrior, notorious for his cruelty, made Samarkand his capital.
23. This last Moorish stronghold in Spain fell in 1492.
24. Henry V won an outstanding victory against the French here in 1415.
25. This English king divided his realm with Guthrum the Dane.
26. Henry II of England was responsible for this Archbishop of Canterbury's death.
27. This palace in Granada is one of the finest examples of Moorish architecture.
28. This famous poem recounts the life of a Geat king.
29. The Frankish king Charles Martel stopped the Muslim advance into western Europe here in 732.
30. In 843 this treaty divided the empire of Charlemagne.

21. Pepin the Short
22. Tamerlane
23. Granada
24. Battle of Agincourt
25. Alfred the Great
26. Thomas Becket
27. The Alhambra
28. Beowulf
29. Battle of Tours
30. Treaty of Verdun

EARLY MODERN HISTORY

Freshman Level

1. He painted the ceiling of the Sistine Chapel.
2. This Italian discovered that falling bodies have equal velocities.
3. This German invented movable type for printing.
4. This Spanish queen was the patron of Columbus.
5. This painting is noted for the subject's mysterious smile.
6. This powerful Florentine family was a patron of the arts.
7. This calendar was introduced in 1582.
8. This victory over Spain established England as a naval power.
9. He was known as the Bard of Avon.
10. His ship was the first to sail around the world.

1. Michelangelo
2. Galileo
3. Johann Gutenberg
4. Isabella
5. "Mona Lisa"
6. Medici
7. Gregorian calendar
8. Defeat of the Armada
9. William Shakespeare
10. Ferdinand Magellan

Graduate Level

11. This city-state was Venice's most serious trade rival.
12. The Ottomans laid seige to this European capital in 1529.
13. Sir Thomas More refused to recognize this king as head of the Church of England.
14. This Spanish writer penned *Don Quixote*.
15. This is Michelangelo's most famous sculpture.
16. He wrote *The Prince*.
17. Shapespeare's *Romeo and Juliet* is set in this Italian city.
18. This Italian city-state was famed for its glassware.
19. This Queen of France was the daughter of Lorenzo de Medici.
20. She was Queen of England during Shakespeare's time.

11. Genoa
12. Vienna
13. Henry V
14. Miguel de Cervantes
15. "David"
16. Machiavelli
17. Verona
18. Venice
19. Catherine de Medici
20. Elizabeth I

Ph.D. Level

21. This genius was Cesare Borgia's military engineer.
22. This Flemish artist painted "Rape of the Sabines."
23. He wrote *The Tragical History of Dr. Faustus*.
24. Henry VIII executed his second wife. She was . . .
25. This church in Rome was completed in 1626.
26. He established the Presbyterian form of Protestantism in Switzerland.
27. Under his rule, the Ottoman empire reached its zenith.
28. He sailed around Africa and discovered a sea route to India.
29. He led the Reformation in Scotland.
30. He published his heliocentric theory of astronomy in 1543.

21. Leonardo da Vinci
22. Peter-Paul Rubens
23. Christopher Marlowe
24. Anne Boleyn
25. St. Peter's Basilica
26. John Calvin
27. Suleiman I
28. Vasco da Gama
29. John Knox
30. Nicolaus Copernicus

AVIATION FIRSTS

Freshman Level

1. 1903 The Wright Brothers made their famous first flight in this plane.
2. 1927 Lindbergh's accomplishment.
3. 1987 This plane made the first nonstop flight around the world without refueling.
4. 1926 He made the first flight over the North Pole.
5. 1919 John Alcock and Arthur Whitten Brown's accomplishment.
6. 1932 She made the first transatlantic solo flight by a woman.
7. 1949 A Boeing B-50A Superfortress accomplished this.
8. 1980 First man-powered craft to fly across English channel.
9. 1978 The first successful transatlantic balloon flight.
10. 1929 Richard Byrd was first to do this.

1. *Flyer*
2. First solo transatlantic flight
3. *Voyager*
4. Richard Byrd
5. First nonstop transatlantic flight
6. Amelia Earhart
7. First round-the-world flight.
8. *Gossamer Albatross*
9. *Double Eagle II*
10. Fly over South Pole

Graduate Level

11. 1782 The Montgolfier brother's accomplishment.
12. 1900 First flight of rigid-frame airships designed by this German.
13. 1921 First use of this nonflammable gas in a balloon.
14. 1922 Harold Harris became first member of Caterpillar Club. Membership is limited to people who have had———.
15. 1976 First regularly scheduled SST (supersonic transport) flight in this plane.
16. 1977 The *Gossamer Condor*, the first successful———.
17. 1933 He made the first round-the-world solo flight.
18. 1939 The German Heinkel HE178 made the first———.
19. 1947 Capt. Chuck Yeager flew the X-1 rocket plane in this first.
20. 1910 Lt. Eugene Ely took off from the *Birmingham* to make the first flight———.

11. First balloon ascension
12. Ferdinand von Zeppelin
13. Helium
14. Life saved by parachute
15. Concorde
16. man-powered aircraft
17. Wiley Post
18. turbojet flight
19. First piloted supersonic flight
20. from shipboard

Ph. D. Level

21. 1937 German pilot Hanna Reitsch made the first successful flight in a———.
22. 1952 A BOAC DeHavilland Comet was used for the first———.
23. 1797 André-Jacques Garnerin bravely did this first.
24. 1980 A balloon, *Joy of Sound*, made the first successful———.
25. 1984 *Rosie O'Grady's Balloon of Peace* made the first———.
26. 1932 Ruth Rowland Nichols became the first woman———.
27. 1909 Louis Bleriot made the first flight———.
28. 1910 Baroness Raymonde de la Roche became the first———.
29. 1908 Unfortunately Thomas Selfridge became the first———.
30. 1980 The *Solar Challenger* made the first———.

21. Helicopter
22. Jetliner service
23. First parachute jump
24. Balloon flight over North Pole
25. Solo transatlantic balloon flight
26. Airline pilot
27. Across English Channel
28. Licensed woman pilot
29. Airplane fatality
30. Long-distance solar-powered flight.

PRE-TWENTIETH CENTURY: GENERAL

Freshman Level

1. He was the ruler of France's First Empire
2. Reputedly, only 23 of 146 prisoners survived an ordeal here.
3. This was Christopher Columbus's birthplace.
4. He is credited with the discovery of Hawaii.
5. The last U.S. president elected in the Nineteenth Century . . .
6. In which city did Jack the Ripper operate?
7. This Portuguese prince sponsored the exploration of Africa's coast.
8. He was King of England from 1760 to 1820.
9. This Englishman defeated Napoleon at Waterloo.
10. This statue was found on the Greek Island of Melos in 1820.

1. Napolean I
2. Black Hole of Calcutta
3. Genoa, Italy
4. James Cook
5. William McKinley
6. London, England
7. Prince Henry

8. George III
9. Duke of Wellington
10. Venus de Milo

Graduate Level

11. Who was executed in 1431?
12. This Roman gladiator's slave was defeated in southern Italy.
13. He tried to blow up the English House of Lords.
14. This Empress of Russia reigned from 1762 to 1796.
15. In 1815 he invented a road surface made of small broken stones compacted into a solid mass.
16. His wife was Roxana. His horse was Bucephalus. He was . . .
17. This famous book was first published in England in 1611.

18. With what cause was William Wilberforce identified?
19. In 1894 this Frenchman was falsely convicted of treason.
20. This South American was called The Liberator.

11. Joan of Arc
12. Spartacus
13. Guy Fawkes
14. Catherine the Great
15. John L. McAdam

16. Alexander the Great
17. King James Version of the Bible
18. Antislavery crusade
19. Alfred Dreyfus
20. Simon Bolivar

Ph.D. Level

21. Who was Alexander the Great's father?
22. He and his son ruled England until the restoration of the monarchy under Charles II.
23. He wrote *An Essay on the Principle of Population.*
24. This British financier had a country named after him.
25. William the Conqueror ordered this census of English property.
26. Where in Rome were the famous chariot races held?
27. This daughter of a pope has been falsely associated with immoral excesses.
28. What was the name of Plato's school?
29. He searched for the Northeast Passage and had a sea named after him.
30. He translated the Bible from Latin into English between 1376 and 1382.

21. King Philip of Macedon
22. Oliver Cromwell

23. Thomas Malthus
24. Cecil J. Rhodes
25. Domesday Book

26. Circus Maximus
27. Lucrezia Borgia

28. The Academy
29. W. Barents

30. John Wycliffe

WARS AND DISASTERS

Freshman Level

1. Napoleon was defeated in this battle in 1815.
2. The commanding general of the Union Army.
3. The second city devastated by an atomic bomb.
4. The conqueror who spread Greek culture as far as India.
5. This ship sank in 1912 after hitting an iceberg.
6. He defeated Rommel at El Alamein.
7. This volcano buried the city of Pompeii.
8. Term for the Nazi annihilation of six million Jews.
9. Carthaginian general who crossed the Alps to invade Italy.
10. He was the top flying ace of World War I.

1. Waterloo
2. Ulysses S. Grant
3. Nagasaki
4. Alexander the Great
5. *Titanic*
6. Montgomery
7. Mt. Vesuvius
8. Holocaust
9. Hannibal
10. Manfred von Richthofen

Graduate Level

11. The longest war in history.
12. The greatest military evacuation in history.
13. Germany's allies in World War I were Austria-Hungary, Bulgaria, and . . .
14. Churchill, Roosevelt, and Stalin met here in 1945.
15. At this battle 10,000 Athenians defeated King Darius' 100,000 men.
16. This was the largest invasion in military history.
17. The greatest known volcanic explosion took place on this island.
18. The struggle for control of supply routes to the British Isles during World War II was called . . .
19. This country won the Six-Day War.
20. At least 25 million people died in Europe between 1337 and 1453 because of this.

11. The 100 Years' War
12. Dunkirk
13. Turkey
14. Yalta
15. Marathon
16. D-Day
17. Santorini
18. The Battle of the Atlantic
19. Israel
20. Black Death (bubonic plague)

Ph.D. Level

21. The Norman duke, William, defeated Harold II of England at this battle.
22. What was "Little Boy"?
23. World War II seige that resulted in over a million deaths.
24. This Italian liner collided with a Swedish ship off Nantucket in 1956.
25. Pan American and KLM Boeing 747's collided on the runway here in 1977.
26. This ship burned at the Toronto docks in 1949, killing 130.
27. This American submarine sank in 1963 killing 129.
28. A dam burst here in 1889 killing 2,209.
29. Germany's allies in World War II were Japan, Italy, Hungary, Bulgaria, Finland, Libya, and . . .
30. In May 1979 a DC-10 crashed here, killing 272.

21. Battle of Hastings
22. Atomic bomb at Hiroshima
23. Leningrad
24. *Andrea Doria*
25. Canary Islands (Tenerife)
26. *Noronic*
27. *Thresher*
28. Johnstown, Pa.
29. Rumania
30. Chicago, Ill.

TWENTIETH CENTURY: GENERAL

Freshman Level

1. This country was finally admitted to the United Nations in 1971.
2. This country captured Berlin in 1945.
3. The British Prime Minister from 1945 to 1951 was ...
4. In 1961 this city was divided by a wall.
5. These three countries occupied West Germany prior to 1949.
6. Iraq invaded this country in 1980.
7. This Egyptian leader was assassinated in 1981.
8. Who was nicknamed Winnie?
9. Britain and Argentina fought over these islands in 1982.
10. Lech Walesa led this Polish union.

1. People's Republic of China
2. U.S.S.R.
3. Clement Attlee
4. Berlin
5. Britain, France, U.S.A.
6. Iran
7. Anwar Sadat
8. Winston Churchill
9. Falklands
10. Solidarity

Graduate Level

11. Which two nations were in the Cod War of 1972–76?
12. Which Chinese dynasty was overthrown in 1911?
13. This king boycotted the wedding of Prince Charles in 1981.
14. This Egyptian President seized the Suez Canal in 1956.
15. This Argentine revolutionary fought alongside Castro.
16. Six nations formed this economic organization in 1958.
17. He performed the first successful heart transplant.
18. President Galtieri was deposed in 1982. Which country did he lead?
19. This Argentinian leader was succeeded by his second wife.
20. He died in 1912 during an expedition to the South Pole.

11. Britain, Iceland
12. Manchu Dynasty
13. King Juan Carlos
14. Gamal Abdel Nasser
15. Che Guevara
16. European Common Market
17. Dr. Christiaan Barnard
18. Argentina
19. Juan Peron
20. Robert F. Scott

Ph.D. Level

21. This was the British flagship during the Falkland Islands dispute.
22. She is the youngest woman ever elected to the British Parliament.
23. In what year does England's lease on Hong Kong expire?
24. Name two of the Big Three leaders who participated in the Treaty of Versailles.
25. Mao's widow led this group.
26. He ruled Portugal from 1932 to 1968.
27. What does SWAPO mean?
28. In what cathedral were Prince Charles and Lady Diana married?
29. The *Titanic* belonged to this shipping line.
30. He became Prime Minister of Jamaica in 1980.

21. *Invincible*
22. Bernadette Devlin
23. 1997
24. L. George, W. Wilson, G. Clemenceau
25. The Gang of Four
26. Antonio Salazar
27. Southwest Africa People's Organization
28. St. Paul's
29. White Star Line
30. Edward Seaga

HOAXES, BLUNDERS, AND ODDITIES

Freshman Level

1. He thought China lay within easy sailing distance west of Europe.
2. Radio program that threw America into a panic in 1938.
3. This city had a $1 billion debt after staging the Olympic Games.
4. Many died because this ship had too few lifeboats.
5. Ford misjudged the market with this classic nonseller.
6. He was paid a fortune for a nonexistent autobiography.
7. Warnings were ignored and this American military disaster resulted.
8. His plans for peace between England and Germany ended in his life imprisonment.
9. He allowed the attempted bugging of the Democratic Committee headquarters.
10. Only 329 of 600 soldiers survived this military blunder.

1. Christopher Columbus
2. "War of the Worlds"
3. Montreal
4. *Titanic*
5. Edsel
6. Clifford Irving
7. Pearl Harbor
8. Rudolf Hess
9. Richard Nixon
10. Charge of Light Brigade

Graduate Level

11. The distribution of this drug caused many birth defects.
12. He admitted to "cheating" on the game show *Twenty-One*.
13. In 1938 he said, "I believe it's peace for our time."
14. This gangster vainly used acid to change his fingerprints.
15. Estimated to cost $5 million, this opera house cost $55 million.
16. Dohn Farynor left an oven on in 1666, causing this fire.
17. Only a horse named Comanche survived this general's foolish attack on Indians.
18. Outnumbered three to one, the Japanese bluffed the English into surrendering this city in 1942.
19. Master hoaxer Ferdinand Waldo Demara was known as . . .
20. Howard Hughes' flying boat only flew once. It was nicknamed . . .

11. Thalidomide
12. Charles Van Doren
13. Neville Chamberlain
14. John Dillinger
15. Sydney Opera House
16. Great Fire of London
17. George Custer
18. Singapore
19. The Great Imposter
20. Spruce Goose

Ph.D. Level

21. Negligence caused the loss of this ship and much oil pollution (1967).
22. Because this pilot flew east from New York instead of west, he was nicknamed . . .
23. Swimmer Sylvia Ester's 100-meter record swim wasn't recognized. Why?
24. New Brunswick gave financial backing to this ill-fated sportscar.
25. The American rescue attempt of Iranian hostages failed largely because of malfunctioning . . .
26. Hiroo Onoda, a World War II Japanese soldier, made longest blunder.
27. John Lee was sentenced to hang, but his sentence was commuted to life imprisonment after this blunder.
28. The archaeological world accepted this phony skull as real.
29. Britain spent 12.5 million pounds on the project but only completed one of these large airliners.
30. This war ace neglected to look behind him and was shot down after 80 air victories.

21. *Torrey Canyon*
22. Wrong-Way Corrigan
23. Swam in the nude
24. Bricklin Special
25. Helicopters
26. Fought until 1974
27. Trap door failed three times
28. Piltdown Man
29. Bristol Brabazon
30. Manfred von Richthofen

THE UNITED STATES: GENERAL

Freshman Level

1. What did Presidents Madison, Monroe, Polk, and Garfield have in common?
2. All the other Presidents had one but Buchanan didn't.
3. This state capital was originally named Fort Orange.
4. Complete the President's name: President Chester Alan ...
5. Where is the Oval Office?
6. President Grover Cleveland dedicated this monument in 1886.
7. He led a raid on Harper's Ferry in 1859.
8. This frontiersman and politician was killed at the Alamo.
9. He established the Dutch claim to New York.
10. He discovered Florida.

1. First name James
2. Wife
3. Albany, New York
4. Arthur
5. The White House
6. Statue of Liberty
7. John Brown
8. Davey Crockett
9. Henry Hudson
10. Juan Ponce de Leon

Graduate Level

11. What ran from St. Joseph, Missouri, to Sacramento, California?
12. This "railroad" had "stations," "conductors," and "lines," but no locomotives.
13. This was one of the most influential books ever written in America and helped to end slavery.
14. The B&O was the first U.S. passenger railroad. What did the letters stand for?
15. He was the first President born outside the original thirteen states.
16. The captain of this American prisoner-of-war camp was hanged for war crimes.
17. What was the earlier name of the Hawaiian Islands?
18. In 1961 a landing was made here in an attempt to liberate Cuba.
19. Where is George Washington buried?
20. This declaration warned European countries not to interfere in the Americas.

11. The Pony Express
12. Underground Railway
13. *Uncle Tom's Cabin*
14. Baltimore & Ohio
15. Abraham Lincoln
16. Andersonville, Georgia
17. Sandwich Islands
18. Bay of Pigs
19. Mount Vernon, Virginia
20. Monroe Doctrine

Ph.D. Level

21. Where would you have seen the Trylon and the Perisphere?
22. Horace Fletcher's most popular theory about nutrition was that each mouthful of food should be ...
23. What movement was Carry Nation associated with in the 1890's?
24. Who was Richard Nixon's running mate in 1960?
25. Who killed Billy the Kid?
26. Name the scandal involving naval oil reserve leases during Harding's term.
27. He killed Alexander Hamilton in a duel.
28. In 1960 this submarine circumnavigated the globe under water.
29. This 1857 Supreme Court decision ruled that a slave could not gain his freedom by being taken out of a slave state.
30. Who directed the attack on the Alamo?

21. New York World's Fair (1939–40)
22. Chewed thirty-two times
23. Temperance movement
24. Henry Cabot Lodge
25. Pat Garrett
26. Teapot Dome Scandal.
27. Aaron Burr
28. *Triton*
29. Dred Scott Decision
30. Santa Anna

U.S. CIVIL WAR

Freshman Level

1. How many years did the war last?
2. General T. J. Jackson was nicknamed . . .
3. The South lost more than 20,000 men, dead and wounded, in this battle.
4. This city was the capital of the Confederacy.
5. How many states fought for the Confederacy?
6. General Lee surrendered to Grant at Appomattox Court House. In which state did this occur?
7. The war began in 1861 with the shelling of this fort in South Carolina.
8. President Lincoln issued a declaration of policy on January 1, 1863. Name it.
9. This was the first state to secede from the Union.
10. His troops left Atlanta in flames.

1. Four
2. Stonewall
3. Gettysburg
4. Richmond, Virginia
5. Eleven
6. Virginia
7. Fort Sumter
8. Emancipation Proclamation
9. South Carolina
10. General Sherman

Graduate Level

11. The outstanding naval figure of the war captured Mobile Bay in 1864. Name him.
12. Whom did the Confederacy elect as President?
13. The *Merrimack* fought this Federal ironclad.
14. This general led the Union forces at the Battle of Antietam.
15. How many states fought for the Union?
16. The North had the "Stars and Stripes," the South had . . .
17. Quote the first five words of the Gettysburg Address.
18. Lincoln said, "I can't spare this man—he fights!" He referred to . . .
19. Armies on the march ate hard biscuits called . . .
20. The Battle of Manassas is known in the North as the Battle of . . .

11. David G. Farragut
12. Jefferson Davis
13. *Monitor*
14. G. B. McClellan
15. Twenty-three
16. "Stars and Bars"
17. Fourscore and seven years ago
18. General Grant
19. Hardtack
20. Bull Run

Ph.D. Level

21. Who said, "War is hell"?
22. The Confederates renamed the *Merrimack*. They called it . . .
23. What was the claim to fame of Walter Williams of Texas?
24. Admiral D. G. Farragut said this when warned of floating mines in the Alabama harbor.
25. "Peace Democrats" were proslavery Northerners who denounced the "war for the Negro." Unionists called them . . .
26. What role did Matthew Brady play in the war?
27. Clara Barton, the "Angel of the Battlefield," founded this organization.
28. To whom was General Lee referring when he said, "He has lost his left arm, but I have lost my right arm"?
29. He was known as The Rock of Chickamauga.
30. Men who enlisted to receive a bounty, then deserted were called . . .

21. William T. Sherman
22. *Virginia*
23. Last surviving veteran
24. "Damn the torpedoes! Full steam ahead!"
25. Copperheads
26. Photographer
27. American Red Cross
28. General T. J. Jackson
29. General G. H. Thomas
30. Bounty jumpers

1950 – 1979

Freshman Level

1. This war began on June 25, 1950.
2. This president ordered American forces into Korea.
3. The Egyptian president who seized the Suez Canal in 1956.
4. In 1951 the American government ended six years of military occupation in this country.
5. The Bay of Pigs fiasco took place in this country in 1961.
6. Russian satellite nation which attempted in 1956 to obtain independence.
7. This country was finally admitted to the United Nations in 1971.
8. U.S. president who ordered the bombing of North Vietnam in 1964.
9. This Chinese leader died in 1976.
10. Nehru's daughter became prime minister of India in 1966. Name her.

1. Korean War
2. Harry S Truman
3. Gamal Abdul Nasser
4. Japan

5. Cuba
6. Hungary

7. People's Republic of China

8. Lyndon B. Johnson

9. Mao Tse-tung
10. Indira Gandhi

Graduate Level

11. This Nazi was released from prison in 1966.
12. Israeli commandos rescued 104 hostages here in 1976.
13. He led 900 followers in a mass suicide in Guyana in 1979.
14. Communists captured this French fortress in 1954.
15. Who was the Communist leader of North Vietnam at the time?
16. He succeeded Stalin in 1953.
17. During the Six-Day War, Israel occupied the Golan Heights. From which country was the territory taken?
18. Israel also took the West Bank, which belonged to . . .
19. This country withdrew from NATO in 1967.
20. In 1961 President Kennedy inaugurated the "Alliance for Progress" plan to assist which area?

11. Albert Speer
12. Entebbe Airport
13. Jim Jones
14. Dien Bien Phu
15. Ho Chi Minh
16. Nikita Khrushchev
17. Syria

18. Jordan
19. France
20. Latin America

Ph.D. Level

21. This secret anti-white society was established in Kenya.
22. What country controlled Angola prior to its independence?
23. In 1976 this leader of Uganda proclaimed himself president for life.
24. The space age began with the launching of this satellite.
25. A UN force was sent to this island in 1964 to maintain peace between the Greek and Turkish residents.
26. Between 1950 and 1965 three countries tested their first atomic devices. They were France, Great Britain, and . . .
27. Mao's widow led an extremist group called . . .
28. In 1955 the Soviet satellites signed this military alliance.
29. This British war hero was killed by IRA bombs.
30. This former Italian prime minister was kidnapped and killed.

21. Mau Mau
22. Portugal
23. Idi Amin

24. Sputnik I
25. Cyprus

26. China

27. Gang of Four
28. Warsaw Pact
29. Earl Mountbatten
30. Aldo Moro

TWENTIETH CENTURY AMERICA

Freshman Level

1. He assassinated President Kennedy.
2. Whose Vice President was Richard Nixon?
3. What foul deed did Mark David Chapman commit in 1980?
4. The St. Valentine's Day massacre took place in this city.
5. This radio program panicked some Americans in 1938.
6. In 1932 he promised a New Deal for America.
7. In 1979 a DC-10 crashed in this city, killing 272.
8. He was the first U.S. President to resign.
9. This senator was noted for anticommunist "witch-hunts."
10. George Wallace was governor of this state.

1. Lee Harvey Oswald
2. Eisenhower
3. Killed John Lennon
4. Chicago
5. "War of the Worlds"
6. F. D. Roosevelt
7. Chicago
8. Richard Nixon
9. Joseph McCarthy
10. Alabama

Graduate Level

11. He was elected to the Presidency eight years after completing his term as Vice President.
12. Following the shooting of Reagan, he declared himself in charge.
13. What "first" took place at Trinity Site, New Mexico?
14. Who was responsible for the "Saturday Night Massacre"?
15. Who led the American Expeditionary Force in World War I?
16. For what crime was Al Capone jailed in 1931?
17. This President's slogan was "He kept us out of war."
18. Who was President Carter's Vice-President?
19. He was the mayor of New York from 1966 to 1974.
20. This American disaster took place in 1906.

11. Richard Nixon
12. Alexander Haig
13. First atomic bomb exploded
14. President Nixon
15. John J. Pershing
16. Tax evasion
17. Woodrow Wilson
18. Walter Mondale
19. John Lindsay
20. San Francisco earthquake

Ph.D. Level

21. This governor was wounded when President Kennedy was killed.
22. He was executed for the murder of Charles Lindbergh, Jr.
23. This U.S. Black Muslim leader was assassinated in 1965.
24. In 1965 blacks rioted in this section of Los Angeles.
25. Who assassinated Martin Luther King, Jr.?
26. This act barred the transporting of women across state lines for immoral purposes.
27. This actor married J. F. Kennedy's sister.
28. He founded the American Nazi Party.
29. These brothers tried to corner the silver market in 1980.

30. This newspaper prematurely declared Dewey winner of the 1948 election.

21. John Connally
22. Bruno R. Hauptmann
23. Malcolm X
24. Watts
25. James Earl Ray
26. Mann Act

27. Peter Lawford
28. G. L. Rockwell
29. Nelson Bunker Hunt and W. Herbert Hunt
30. Chicago *Tribune*

TWENTIETH CENTURY AMERICA: INTERNATIONAL EVENTS

Freshman Level

1. Name the two cities at opposite ends of Lindbergh's flight.
2. This President dismissed General MacArthur.
3. This attack took place on December 7, 1941.
4. The U.S. embassy in this city was bombed in 1983.
5. Chinese athlete Hu Na gained asylum in the U.S. in 1983. In which sport does she excel?
6. This President visited Communist China in 1972.
7. This President ordered American forces into Korea.
8. Sargent Shriver was the first director of this organization.
9. What took 33 hours, 30 minutes, 29.8 seconds in 1927?
10. He was the most celebrated U.S. air ace in World War I.

1. New York, Paris
2. Harry S Truman
3. Pearl Harbor
4. Beirut
5. Tennis

6. Richard Nixon
7. Harry S Truman
8. Peace Corps
9. Lindbergh's flight
10. Edward Rickenbacker

Graduate Level

11. A U.N. force was sent to this island in 1964 to maintain peace.
12. This President ordered the bombing of Viet Nam in 1964.
13. Which area was J. F. Kennedy's Alliance for Progress designed to assist?
14. In what year did the U.S. enter World War I?
15. This U.S. Secretary of State won the Nobel Peace Prize in 1973.
16. He led nine hundred followers in a mass suicide in 1979.
17. This President pardoned Tokyo Rose.
18. This ship was sunk by Germany's U-20 submarine.
19. What is the Washington-Moscow hotline called?
20. A U.S. anticommunist organization is named after this man.

11. Cypress
12. Lyndon B. Johnson
13. Latin America

14. 1917
15. Henry Kissinger
16. Jim Jones
17. Gerald Ford
18. *Lusitania*
19. Molink
20. John Birch

Ph.D. Level

21. This Canadian ambassador helped to rescue six American hostages.
22. North Korea seized this U.S. Navy ship in 1968.
23. On January 20, 1981, how many hostages were released from Iran?
24. This was the code name for the U.S. rescue mission in Iran.
25. The Japanese freighter *Nissho Maru* made news in the 80's. Why?
26. What was the *Enola Gay*?
27. This World War I hero received fifty medals.
28. This U.S. submarine sank in 1963 killing 129.
29. Who commanded the U.S. forces in Viet Nam?
30. He piloted the U-2 spy plane shot down over Russia in 1960.

21. Kenneth Taylor
22. *Pueblo*
23. Fifty-two

24. Eagle Claw
25. Sunk by U.S. submarine

26. B-29 at Hiroshima
27. Alvin York
28. *Thresher*
29. William C. Westmoreland
30. Francis Gary Powers

APRIL 15, THE TITANIC SINKS

Freshman Level

1. What was the *Titanic*'s planned destination?
2. It departed from this English port.
3. How many voyages had the *Titanic* completed prior to the disaster?
4. In 1987 a safe from the *Titanic* was opened on television. Who hosted the show?
5. At approximately what time did the collision occur?
6. To what line did the *Titanic* belong?
7. The *Titanic* was first to use this new distress signal.
8. There were over 2,200 on board. About how many perished?
9. Walter Lord's famous book was titled———.
10. Lord's second *Titanic* book (1986) was titled———.

1. New York City
2. Southhampton
3. None (maiden voyage)
4. Telly Savalas
5. Midnight
6. White Star Line
7. SOS
8. 1,500
9. *A Night to Remember*
10. *The Night Lives On*

Graduate Level

11. In what year did the disaster occur?
12. A priceless jeweled copy of this book went down with the ship.
13. What other problem had the *Titanic* had during its entire voyage?
14. Where are the graves of the unclaimed corpses that were recovered?
15. What occurred in September 1985?
16. The supposed rule for placing passengers on lifeboats was———?
17. Name the male star of the 1953 film, *Titanic*.
18. It could have been worse. How?
19. What was unusual about one of the four huge funnels?
20. What part did Fred Fleet play in the disaster?

11. 1912
12. The *Rubaiyat*
13. A fire in coal bunker
14. Halifax
15. *Titanic* located and photographed.
16. "Women and children first"
17. Clifton Webb
18. *Titanic* was only two-thirds full.
19. It was a dummy.
20. Sighted the iceberg

Ph. D. Level

21. In 1898 a novel was written about a huge ship that hit an iceberg on its maiden voyage and sank. What was the ship called?
22. Thomas Andrews perished. Who was he?
23. This famous millionaire also perished.
24. What was the name of the *Titanic*'s sister ship?
25. Name the first ship to reach the scene.
26. This nearby ship made no attempt to reach the wreck.
27. What role did the ship *Mackay-Bennett* play in the disaster?
28. What was the captain's name?
29. What was omitted from the launching of the *Titanic*?
30. What song was the orchestra playing as the ship sank?

21. *Titan*
22. The *Titanic*'s builder
23. John Jacob Astor
24. *Olympic*
25. The *Carpathia*
26. The *Californian*
27. Recovered bodies
28. Edward Smith
29. A christening ceremony
30. "Autumn"

IT HAPPENED HERE
What event took place at the given time and place?

Freshman Level

1. July 29, 1981	St. Paul's Cathedral	1.	Charles and Di wedding
2. December 22, 1984	New York subway	2.	Bernard Goetz shooting
3. December 8, 1980	Outside Dakota Hotel, New York	3.	John Lennon shot
4. April 14, 1865	Ford Theater, Washington, D.C.	4.	Lincoln assassinated
5. December 3, 1984	Union Carbide plant, Bhopal, India	5.	Toxic gas fumes kill over 2,500 people
6. May 13, 1981	St. Paul's Square	6.	John Paul II shot
7. July 27, 1934	Outside Biograph Theater, Chicago	7.	John Dillinger killed
8. February 14, 1929	2122 North Clark Street, Chicago	8.	St. Valentine's Day Massacre
9. June 5, 1944	Omaha Beach, France	9.	D-Day landings
10. June 17, 1972	Democratic National Committee Headquarters, Washington, D.C.	10.	Watergate break-in

Graduate Level

11. June 5, 1968	Ambassador Hotel, Los Angeles	11.	R. Kennedy assassinated
12. April 15–17, 1969	600-acre farm of Max Yasgur in Bethel, New York	12.	Woodstock Music Festival
13. March 30, 1981	Outside Washington Hilton Hotel	13.	President Reagan shot
14. November 22, 1963	411 Elm Street, Dallas, Texas	14.	Oswald shot Kennedy
15. August 4, 1944	263 Princengracht, Amsterdam	15.	Anne Frank arrested
16. April 4, 1968	Lorraine Motel, Memphis	16.	Martin Luther King, Jr. assassinated
17. August 8, 1969	10050 Cielo Drive, Los Angeles	17.	Sharon Tate murdered
18. October 23, 1983	Aviation Safety Building, Beirut	18.	241 marines killed in bomb attack
19. May 28, 1987	Red Square, Moscow	19.	Cessna plane landed
20. May 29, 1985	Heysel Stadium, Brussels	20.	Soccer riot (thirty-eight killed)

Ph. D. Level

21. October 31, 1984	1 Safdarjang Road, New Delhi	21.	Indira Gandhi assassinated
22. May 4, 1985	Bitburg military cemetery, Germany	22.	President Reagan lays wreath
23. July 30, 1975	Manchus Red Fox Restaurant, Detroit	23.	Hoffa disappeared
24. September 18, 1975	625 Morris Street, San Francisco	24.	Patty Hearst found
25. May 15, 1972	Laurel Shopping Center, Laurel, Md.	25.	George Wallace shot
26. February 21, 1965	Audubon Ballroom, New York	26.	Malcolm X assassinated
27. August 4, 1892	92 Secord St., Fall River, Massachusetts	27.	Lizzie Borden murders
28. October 8, 1871	558 DeKoven Street, Chicago	28.	Mrs. O'Leary's barn (Chicago fire).
29. September 5, 1921	St. Francis Hotel, San Francisco	29.	Fatty Arbuckle scandal
30. August 5, 1962	12305 Fifth Helena Dr., Los Angeles	30.	Marilyn Monroe died

WORLD WAR II

Freshman Level

1. Name the first city hit by an atomic bomb.
2. Which country did Germany attack on September 1, 1939?
3. Who was the Russian leader during World War II?
4. Germany and its allies were known as the ...
5. What was the German air force called?
6. He offered only "blood, toil, tears, and sweat."
7. He led Germany's Afrika Corps.
8. This incident brought the U.S. into the war.
9. This was Britain's most famous fighter plane.
10. He called December 7, 1941, "a date which will live in infamy."

1. Hiroshima
2. Poland
3. Joseph Stalin
4. Axis
5. Luftwaffe
6. Winston Churchill
7. Erwin Rommel
8. Attack on Pearl Harbor
9. Spitfire
10. F. D. Roosevelt

Graduate Level

11. What did the acronym WAC mean?
12. This U.S. naval victory ended Japan's expansion eastward.
13. For seven months after the Polish campaign of 1939 the Germans and the Allies fought no important land battles. Newspapers called the war in the west the ...
14. This was the most famous German dive bomber.
15. Hitler's deputy flew to Great Britain in May 1941. Name him.
16. The Germans lost almost an entire army in this Russian battle.
17. The Germans developed the V-1 rocket. The British called it the ...
18. The last-stand German onslaught in the Ardennes was called ...
19. The start of the invasion of Europe was called ...
20. He was the supreme commander of the Allied Expeditionary Force.

11. Women's Army Corps
12. Midway
13. Phony War

14. Stuka
15. Rudolf Hess
16. Battle of Stalingrad
17. Buzz bomb

18. Battle of the Bulge
19. D-Day
20. Dwight D. Eisenhower

Ph.D. Level

21. William Joyce made propaganda broadcasts for Germany. He was known as ...
22. The attack on Russia in 1941 was named ...
23. This was A. C. McAuliffe's reply when asked to surrender at Bastogne.
24. The Japanese surrendered aboard this ship.
25. This German pocket battleship was scuttled in Montevideo harbor.
26. This word describes the Nazi annihilation of Jews.
27. Who were the opposing commanders at El Alamein?

28. This name was given to the Japanese suicide attack planes.
29. The undisclosed fact that the Allies had broken the enemy ciphers became known as the ...
30. The most famous picture of the war was taken on this island.

21. Lord Haw-Haw

22. Operation Barbarossa
23. "Nuts!"

24. U.S.S. *Missouri*
25. *Graf Spee*

26. Holocaust
27. Rommel and Montgomery

28. Kamikaze (Divine Wind)
29. Ultra Secret

30. Iwo Jima

ENTERTAINMENT

GENERAL: NUMBER ONE

Freshman Level

1. He played in the film version of *South Pacific* and starred on Broadway in *Tea and Sympathy*.
2. This role made Jerry Mathers famous.
3. This director fled the United States in 1978 to avoid prosecution on a morals charge.
4. Although best known for his tough guy roles, his final film was *Soylent Green*.
5. He was Baretta.
6. These two female singers combined to make the hit record "Enough is Enough."
7. The Sex Pistols helped introduce this new form of music.
8. Jane Fonda and Jack Lemmon starred in this 1979 movie about a nuclear accident.
9. John Travolta played Bud and Debra Winger played Sissy in . . .
10. Ten years after she posed in the nude, *Playboy* published the pictures of this TV star.

1. John Kerr
2. The Beaver
3. Roman Polanski
4. Edward G. Robinson
5. Robert Blake
6. Donna Summer and Barbra Streisand
7. Punk rock
8. *The China Syndrome*
9. *Urban Cowboy*
10. Suzanne Somers

Graduate Level

11. What do Heather Menzies, Duane Chase, and Angela Cartwright have in common?
12. He played Ozzie and Harriet's neighbor on TV during the '50s.
13. He was the boy who played Rin Tin Tin's master on TV.
14. Millie Perkins catapulted to fame when she was chosen to play this movie role.
15. Who were Billy Gray, Lauren Chapin, and Elinor Donahue?
16. What was William Thomas's role in the "Our Gang" films?
17. Who directed the epic film, *Birth of a Nation*?
18. He played in *Waiting for Godot* and *The Seven Year Itch*.
19. There were two major unions involved in the 1980 actors' strike. One of them was the American Federation of Television and Radio Artists. What was the other union?
20. She is known for her Polaroid commercials with James Garner.

11. They played children in *The Sound of Music*
12. Lyle Talbot
13. Lee Aaker
14. Anne Frank
15. Children in *Father Knows Best*
16. Buckwheat
17. D. W. Griffith
18. Tom Ewell
19. Screen Actors Guild
20. Mariette Hartley

Ph.D. Level

21. This actor played opposite Claudette Colbert in *No Time For Love* and in 1954 married the mother of his third wife.
22. Who were Joseph Curtin and Alice Frost of radio fame?
23. The film crew gave the 25-foot mechanical shark used in *Jaws* this nickname.
24. Who was the feline star of the first major X-rated cartoon?
25. Who does the voice of Donald Duck?
26. She married Andre Weinfeld in 1980.
27. Ed Asner won an Emmy for his role in this TV series in 1977.
28. Luise Rainer won Oscars in 1936 and 1937. Name one of the films.
29. Charles Laughton, Lon Chaney, and Anthony Quinn have all played this role in the movies.
30. What is the stage name of Greta Gustafson?

21. Rod Cameron
22. Mr. and Mrs. North
23. Bruce
24. Fritz the Cat
25. Clarence Nash
26. Raquel Welch
27. *Roots*
28. *The Great Ziegfeld; The Good Earth*
29. Quasimodo
30. Greta Garbo

GENERAL: NUMBER TWO

Freshman Level

1. Name the movie based on the play *Pygmalion*.
2. He won the best actor award for his role in *True Grit*.
3. This movie starring Marlon Brando won the best picture award for 1972.
4. During the '30s he was famous for his profile.
5. He starred in *City Lights*.
6. Name a musical film named after a state.
7. She starred in the 1952 film *Niagara*.
8. She won the best actress award for her role in *Butterfield 8*.
9. This movie won the best picture Oscar for 1981.
10. This was the first animated talking picture.

1. *My Fair Lady*
2. John Wayne
3. *The Godfather*
4. John Barrymore
5. Charlie Chaplin
6. *Oklahoma*
7. Marilyn Monroe
8. Elizabeth Taylor
9. *Chariots of Fire*
10. *Steamboat Willie*

Graduate Level

11. What was Debbie Boone's big hit of 1978?
12. The first full-length color cartoon talking picture.
13. He played the deputy sheriff on the *Andy Griffith Show*.
14. This movie directed by Woody Allen won the best picture Oscar for 1978.
15. This actress made her stage debut as Regina in *The Little Foxes*.
16. The play with the longest Broadway run.
17. She portrayed Jeannie in *I Dream of Jeannie*.
18. She won the best actress award for her role in *Coming Home*.
19. This group had a hit with *Saturday Night Fever*.
20. He won the best actor award for his role in *Patton*.

11. "You Light Up My Life"
12. *Snow White and the Seven Dwarfs*
13. Don Knotts
14. *Annie Hall*
15. Elizabeth Taylor
16. *Grease*
17. Barbara Eden
18. Jane Fonda
19. Bee Gees
20. George C. Scott

Ph.D. Level

21. The longest-running TV program.
22. This film won the most Oscars.
23. He won the best actor award for his role in *Network*.
24. This film won the first best picture award, in 1928.
25. Who wrote *Cat on a Hot Tin Roof*?
26. He hosted *What's My Line?*
27. This was the family name in *The Beverly Hillbillies*.
28. Billy Joel won the best song Grammy for 1978 with this song.
29. He was the first major rock star to perform in the USSR.
30. Bill Robinson, a tap dancer who held the world's record for running 100 yards backwards, was better known as . . .

21. *Meet the Press*
22. *Ben Hur*
23. Peter Finch
24. *Wings*
25. Tennessee Williams
26. John Daly
27. Clampett
28. "Just the Way You Are"
29. Elton John
30. Bojangles

MOVIES: TITLE ROLES

Name the person who portrayed the title role.

Freshman Level

1.	*Coal Miner's Daughter*	1. Sissy Spacek
2.	*The Godfather*	2. Marlon Brando
3.	*The Paleface*	3. Bob Hope
4.	*The Hustler*	4. Paul Newman
5.	*The Graduate*	5. Dustin Hoffman
6.	*The Third Man*	6. Orson Welles
7.	*Lawrence of Arabia*	7. Peter O'Toole
8.	*The Jackie Robinson Story*	8. Jackie Robinson
9.	*Cool Hand Luke*	9. Paul Newman
10.	*The Man With the Golden Arm*	10. Frank Sinatra

Graduate Level

11.	*The Buster Keaton Story*	11. Donald O'Connor
12.	*The Babe Ruth Story*	12. William Bendix
13.	*Mr. Deeds Goes to Town*	13. Gary Cooper
14.	*The Candidate*	14. Robert Redford
15.	*The French Lieutenant's Woman*	15. Meryl Streep
16.	*The Goodbye Girl*	16. Marsha Mason
17.	*The Man in the Gray Flannel Suit*	17. Gregory Peck
18.	*Goodbye, Mr. Chips* (1939)	18. Robert Donat
19.	*A Man for All Seasons*	19. Paul Scofield
20.	*A Man Called Horse*	20. Richard Harris

Ph.D. Level

21.	*The Elephant Man*	21. John Hurt
22.	*The Court Jester*	22. Danny Kaye
23.	*The Incredible Shrinking Woman*	23. Lily Tomlin
24.	*Man of La Mancha*	24. Peter O'Toole
25.	*The Deer Hunter*	25. Robert De Niro
26.	*The Spy Who Came in from the Cold*	26. Richard Burton
27.	*The Merry Widow* (1934)	27. Jeanette MacDonald
28.	*The Gambler*	28. James Caan
29.	*Good Neighbor Sam*	29. Jack Lemmon
30.	*The Man Who Came to Dinner*	30. Monty Woolley

MOVIES: SETTINGS, NUMBER ONE

Name the country or territory in which each movie takes place.

Freshman Level

1. 1971 — *Straw Dogs*
2. 1964 — *The Night of the Iguana*
3. 1960 — *The Sundowners*
4. 1968 — *The Lion in Winter*
5. 1953 — *House of Wax*
6. 1971 — *Walkabout*
7. 1954 — *The Bridges at Toko-Ri*
8. 1975 — *The Day of the Locust*
9. 1968 — *Romeo and Juliet*
10. 1964 — *Topkapi*

1. Britain
2. Mexico
3. Australia
4. England
5. France
6. Australia
7. North Korea
8. U.S.A.
9. Italy
10. Turkey

Graduate Level

11. 1942 — *The Moon and Sixpence*
12. 1973 — *Papillion*

13. 1972 — *Cabaret*
14. 1969 — *100 Rifles*
15. 1964 — *Behold a Pale Horse*
16. 1974 — *Gold*
17. 1957 — *The Bridge on the River Kwai*
18. 1966 — *What Did You Do in the War, Daddy?*
19. 1951 — *The Bullfighter and the Lady*
20. 1944 — *Dragon Seed*

11. Tahiti
12. Devil's Island (French Guiana)
13. Germany
14. Mexico
15. Spain
16. South Africa
17. Burma
18. Italy
19. Mexico
20. China

Ph.D. Level

21. 1970 — *Luna*
22. 1943 — *The Moon is Down*
23. 1951 — *Cry the Beloved Country*
24. 1942 — *The Black Swan*
25. 1967 — *Elvira Madigan*
26. 1958 — *Kings Go Forth*
27. 1970 — *Ned Kelly*
28. 1967 — *The Comedians*
29. 1970 — *The McKenzie Break*
30. 1961 — *A Town Without Pity*

21. Italy
22. Norway
23. South Africa
24. Jamaica
25. Denmark
26. France
27. Australia
28. Haiti
29. Scotland
30. West Germany

MOVIES: SETTINGS, NUMBER TWO

Name the city in which each movie takes place.

Freshman Level

1. 1970 — *The Out of Towners*
2. 1956 — *Anastasia*
3. 1938 — *The Great Waltz*
4. 1975 — *Three Days of the Condor*
5. 1972 — *The King of Marvin Gardens*
6. 1970 — *The Only Game in Town*
7. 1939 — *Ninotchka*
8. 1974 — *The Towering Inferno*
9. 1961 — *Two Women*
10. 1978 — *The Brinks Job*

1. New York
2. Paris
3. Vienna
4. New York
5. Atlantic City
6. Las Vegas
7. Paris
8. San Francisco
9. Rome
10. Boston

Graduate Level

11. 1955 — *Love Is a Many Spendored Thing*
12. 1963 — *The V.I.P.s*
13. 1974 — *The Death Wish*
14. 1972 — *The New Centurions*
15. 1955 — *The Man with the Golden Arm*
16. 1960 — *Ocean's Eleven*
17. 1953 — *The City That Never Sleeps*
18. 1961 — *One, Two, Three*
19. 1966 — *The Fortune Cookie*
20. 1982 — *The Blade Runner*

11. Hong Kong
12. London
13. New York
14. Los Angeles
15. Chicago
16. Las Vegas
17. Chicago
18. West Berlin
19. Cleveland
20. Los Angeles

Ph.D. Level

21. 1950 — *Panic in the Streets*
22. 1961 — *A Raisin in the Sun*
23. 1963 — *The Prize*
24. 1943 — *Watch on the Rhine*
25. 1981 — *Absence of Malice*
26. 1965 — *Young Cassidy*
27. 1946 — *Gilda*
28. 1972 — *Fuzz*
29. 1945 — *The Body Snatchers*
30. 1978 — *Invasion of the Body Snatchers*

21. New Orleans
22. Chicago
23. Stockholm
24. Washington
25. Miami
26. Dublin
27. Buenos Aires
28. Boston
29. Edinburgh
30. San Francisco

MOVIES: GENERAL

Freshman Level

1. He played King Arthur in the movie version of *Camelot*.
2. She played the lead role in *Coal Miner's Daughter*.
3. She is the real country music star portrayed in the film.
4. The Village People made their movie debut in this film.
5. In this movie James Cagney played George M. Cohan.
6. This was Errol Flynn's first swashbuckling film.
7. In which Disney movie is the song "So This Is Love"?
8. He played Superman in the 1978 movie version.
9. She played Lois Lane in the same film.
10. This was the Beatles' first film.

1. Richard Harris
2. Sissy Spacek
3. Loretta Lynn
4. *Can't Stop the Music*
5. *Yankee Doodle Dandy*
6. *Captain Blood*
7. *Cinderella*
8. Christopher Reeve
9. Margot Kidder
10. *A Hard Day's Night*

Graduate Level

11. He played eight roles in *Kind Hearts and Coronets*.
12. In this James Bond movie the climax occurs on the Orient Express.
13. This was Sean Connery's first James Bond film.
14. What was Sir Alec Guinness's role in *Star Wars*?
15. What is the name of Luke's strange little adviser in *The Empire Strikes Back*?
16. Who was Nelson Eddy's most popular singing partner?
17. In this movie Nelson and his partner sing "Ah, Sweet Mystery of Life."
18. Who co-starred with Nelson Eddy in *The Chocolate Soldier*?
19. At the end of this movie Edward G. Robinson asks, "Is this the end of Rico?"
20. Marilyn Monroe, Betty Grable, and Lauren Bacall starred in this 1953 movie.

11. Alec Guinness
12. *From Russia with Love*
13. *Doctor No*
14. Obi-wan Kenobi
15. Yoda
16. Jeanette MacDonald
17. *Naughty Marietta*
18. Risë Stevens
19. *Little Caesar*
20. *How to Marry a Millionaire*

Ph.D. Level

21. In this 1953 movie Ann Miller sang "Tom, Dick, and Harry."
22. This film shows the Rolling Stones' concert at Altamont.
23. This was the name of the boat in *Showboat*.
24. Who played the piano player, Sam, in *Casablanca*?
25. The Who's rock concert stars Elton John. It's called . . .
26. This is Led Zeppelin's movie (1976).

27. Elvis fell in love with a nun in the movie *Change of Habit*. Who played the nun?
28. What is Hawkeye's full name in *M*A*S*H*?

29. Who played Hawkeye in the movie version?
30. Alan Ladd starred in this classic western (1953).

21. *Kiss Me Kate*
22. *Gimme Shelter*
23. *Cotton Blossom*
24. Dooley Wilson
25. *Tommy*
26. *The Song Remains the Same*
27. Mary Tyler Moore
28. Benjamin Franklin Pierce
29. Donald Sutherland
30. *Shane*

FILM FIRST

Freshman Level

1. The first movie to win the Best Picture Oscar.
2. The first color film to win Best Picture Oscar.
3. The first feature-length cartoon.

4. The first actress depicted on a postage stamp.
5. The first film musical.
6. The first talking cartoon.
7. The first black to win an Oscar.

8. The first issue of this movie fan magazine was in 1912.
9. Charlie Chaplin's first sound film (music but no dialogue).
10. First actor and son to receive Oscars for the same film.

1. *Wings*
2. *Gone with the Wind*
3. *Snow White and the Seven Dwarfs*
4. Grace Kelly
5. *The Jazz Singer*
6. *Steamboat Willie*
7. Hattie McDaniel (*GWTW*)
8. *Photoplay*
9. *City Lights*
10. Walter and John Huston *Treasure of Sierra Madre*)

Graduate Level

11. The first film presented in 3-D.
12. The first color film presented in 3-D.
13. The first film presented in Cinemascope.
14. The first science fiction film.
15. John C. Rice and May Irwin were the first to do this on film.
16. America's first film serial.
17. The first western film with a plot and featuring a holdup.

18. The first movie premiere festivities to be televised.
19. The first film to be screened at the White House.
20. The first to receive Best Actor Oscars.

11. *Bwana Devil*
12. *House of Wax*
13. *The Robe*
14. *A Trip to the Moon*
15. *Kiss* (1896)
16. *The Perils of Pauline*
17. *The Great Train Robbery*
18. Opening of *GWTW*
19. *Birth of a Nation*
20. Emil Jannings and Janet Gaynor.

Ph. D. Level

21. The first western starring John Wayne.
22. The first film presented simultaneously in major cities throughout the world.
23. Thomas Edison's Black Maria was the first of these in the United States.
24. The first musical movie with a completely original score.

25. The first all-talking film in color.
26. The first all-talking film.
27. The first color cartoon.

28. The first film produced with Dolby Sound.
29. The first closeup was of Fred Ott doing this.
30. The first Western hero.

21. *The Big Trail*
22. *On the Beach*

23. Motion Picture Studio

24. *The Broadway Melody*

25. *On with the Show*
26. *Lights of New York*
27. *The Debut of Thomas Kat*
28. *The Quiet Revolution*
29. Sneezing
30. Bronco Billy Anderson

MOVIES: THE FILMS OF RONALD REAGAN

Complete the Ronald Reagan film title by supplying the last word.

Freshman Level

1. *Bedtime for ...*
2. *King's ...*
3. *The Hasty ...*
4. *The Girl from Jones ...*
5. *This is the ...*
6. *Dark ...*
7. *Brother ...*
8. *Million Dollar ...*
9. *It's a Great ...*
10. *Prisoner of ...*

1. *Bonzo*
2. *Row*
3. *Heart*
4. *Beach*
5. *Army*
6. *Victory*
7. *Rat*
8. *Baby*
9. *Feeling*
10. *War*

Graduate Level

11. *Hollywood ...*
12. *Hell's ...*
13. *Swing Your ...*
14. *International ...*
15. *Desperate ...*
16. *Stallion ...*
17. *Storm ...*
18. *Hellcats of the ...*
19. *Tropic ...*
20. *Angels Wash Their ...*

11. *Hotel*
12. *Kitchen*
13. *Lady*
14. *Squadron*
15. *Journey*
16. *Road*
17. *Warnings*
18. *Navy*
19. *Zone*
20. *Faces*

Ph.D. Level

21. *Cowboy from ...*
22. *Girls on ...*
23. *Going ...*
24. *An Angel from ...*
25. *Murder in the ...*
26. *The Bad ...*
27. *Naughty but ...*
28. *The Last ...*
29. *The Winning ...*
30. *Tennessee's ...*

21. *Brooklyn*
22. *Probation*
23. *Places*
24. *Texas*
25. *Air*
26. *Man*
27. *Nice*
28. *Outpost*
29. *Team*
30. *Partner*

MOVIES: COLORFUL TITLES

Name the movie. Each title contains a color.

Freshman Level

1. A young couple are shipwrecked on a tropic isle.
2. A boy and a horse form a friendship following a shipwreck.
3. About a plot to blow up the Super Bowl.
4. About a German World War I ace's dogfighting adventures.
5. About a teacher's harrowing experiences in a New York school.
6. Rival jewel thieves are pursued by a bumbling police inspector.
7. The heroes try to save Pepperland from the Blue Meanies.
8. A soldier returns to islands to work at a tourist agency.
9. The hero aids victims of the French Revolution.
10. Army buddies boost the popularity of a winter resort.

1. *The Blue Lagoon*
2. *The Black Stallion*
3. *Black Sunday*
4. *The Blue Max*
5. *The Blackboard Jungle*
6. *The Pink Panther*
7. *Yellow Submarine*
8. *Blue Hawaii*
9. *The Scarlet Pimpernel*
10. *White Christmas*

Graduate Level

11. A melodrama about autoworkers who discover their own union is ripping them off.
12. A young ballerina and a neophyte composer are taken under the wing of an impresario.
13. A youth runs from his first Civil War battle.
14. In 2022 New York is polluted and overcrowded.
15. A scathing satire on future society.
16. This cliche salute to the Special Forces stars John Wayne and David Janssen.
17. About a spinster teacher bringing education to a Wales mining community.
18. A Madison Avenue executive struggles to get ahead and find meaning in his home life.
19. A blind girl falls in love with a black man.
20. About the romance in the lives of a trio of owners of a car.

11. *Blue Collar*
12. *The Red Shoes*
13. *The Red Badge of Courage*
14. *Soylent Green*
15. *Clockwork Orange*
16. *The Green Berets*
17. *The Corn is Green*
18. *The Man in the Grey Flannel Suit*
19. *A Patch of Blue*
20. *The Yellow Rolls Royce*

Ph.D. Level

21. A stuffy professor falls for a cabaret singer.
22. Love is forfeited for success in the court of Charles II.
23. A government agent tries to persuade Indians to move to a reservation.
24. A woman accused of murder takes a columnist's offer of help.
25. An account of a supply unit working behind the German lines.
26. About two sisters after the same man in New Zealand.
27. A woman wears the mark of adulteress in Salem.
28. Tale of a U.S. air crew shot down during a Tokyo raid.
29. A small stockholder tries to oust a crooked board of directors.
30. Nuns start a mission in the Himalayas.

21. *The Blue Angel*
22. *Forever Amber*
23. *White Feather*
24. *The Blue Gardenia*
25. *Red Ball Express*
26. *Green Dolphin Street*
27. *The Scarlet Letter*
28. *The Purple Heart*
29. *The Solid Gold Cadillac*
30. *Black Narcissus*

ACTORS AND ACTRESSES

Freshman Level

1. He was the shark hunter in *Jaws* (1975).
2. He played James Bond in *Casino Royale* (1967).
3. He starred in *The Candidate* (1972).
4. She starred in the film version of *Hello Dolly* (1969).
5. These two top male dancers appeared together in *Ziegfeld Follies* (1946).
6. He starred in *The Jolson Story* (1946).
7. She had the female lead in *The King and I* (1956).
8. He starred in the movie *The Sound of Music* (1965).
9. He starred in *Sleuth* (1972) along with Laurence Olivier.
10. He starred in *The Paleface* (1948).

1. Robert Shaw
2. David Niven
3. Robert Redford
4. Barbra Streisand
5. Gene Kelly, Fred Astaire
6. Larry Parks
7. Deborah Kerr
8. Christopher Plummer
9. Michael Caine
10. Bob Hope

Graduate Level

11. He played Gunga Din in the 1939 movie of the same name.
12. He had the lead in *The Sea Wolf* (1941).
13. He co-starred with Orson Welles in *Citizen Kane* (1941).
14. She starred in the movie *Sweet Charity* (1969).
15. This female singer starred in *Finian's Rainbow* (1968).
16. He played the lead in *Brannigan* (1975).
17. He starred in *Jeremiah Johnson* (1972).
18. He starred in *The Absent-Minded Professor* (1961).
19. She had the title role in *Harlow* (1965).
20. She starred in *How Green Was My Valley* (1941).

11. Sam Jaffe
12. Edward G. Robinson
13. Joseph Cotton
14. Shirley MacLaine
15. Petula Clark
16. John Wayne
17. Robert Redford
18. Fred MacMurray
19. Carol Baker
20. Maureen O'Hara

Ph.D. Level

21. In *The Naked Prey* (1966) he portrayed a naked man running for his life in the wilds of Africa.
22. He was the ship captain in *The Poseidon Adventure* (1972).
23. He played secret agent Harry Palmer in *The Ipcress File*.
24. He was the captain in *Captain Nemo and the Underwater City* (1969).
25. He played Ava Gardner's father in *Earthquake* (1974).
26. He starred in the 1938 musical *Alexander's Ragtime Band*.
27. This tenor played a romantic singing role in *A Night at the Opera* (1935).
28. He played the role of the Oriental detective, Mr. Moto.
29. He starred in *The Buster Keaton Story* (1957).
30. He starred in *Raiders of the Lost Ark* (1981).

21. Cornel Wilde
22. Leslie Nielson
23. Michael Caine
24. Robert Ryan
25. Lorne Green
26. Tyrone Power
27. Allan Jones
28. Peter Lorre
29. Donald O'Connor
30. Harrison Ford

OSCARS: BEST PICTURES

Given the year and the leading actors/actresses, name the movie.

Freshman Level

1.	1977 Woody Allen, Diane Keaton	1. *Annie Hall*
2.	1973 Paul Newman, Robert Redford	2. *The Sting*
3.	1970 George C. Scott, Karl Malden	3. *Patton*
4.	1968 Ron Moody, Oliver Reed	4. *Oliver*
5.	1953 Burt Lancaster, Montgomery Clift	5. *From Here to Eternity*
6.	1964 Rex Harrison, Audrey Hepburn	6. *My Fair Lady*
7.	1976 Sylvester Stallone, Talia Shire	7. *Rocky*
8.	1962 Peter O'Toole, Alec Guinness	8. *Lawrence of Arabia*
9.	1965 Julie Andrews, Christopher Plummer	9. *The Sound of Music*
10.	1969 Dustin Hoffman, Jon Voight	10. *Midnight Cowboy*

Graduate Level

11.	1975 Jack Nicholson, Louise Fletcher	11. *One Flew Over the Cuckoo's Nest*
12.	1972 Marlon Brando, Al Pacino	12. *The Godfather*
13.	1967 Sidney Poitier, Rod Steiger	13. *In the Heat of the Night*
14.	1974 Al Pacino, Robert Duvall	14. *The Godfather, Part Two*
15.	1971 Gene Hackman, Fernando Rey	15. *The French Connection*
16.	1963 Albert Finney, Susannah York	16. *Tom Jones*
17.	1961 Natalie Wood, Richard Beymer	17. *West Side Story*
18.	1959 Charlton Heston, Stephen Boyd	18. *Ben Hur*
19.	1960 Jack Lemmon, Shirley MacLaine	19. *The Apartment*
20.	1966 Paul Scolfield, Wendy Hiller	20. *A Man for All Seasons*

Ph.D. Level

21.	1958 Leslie Caron, Maurice Chevalier	21. *Gigi*
22.	1954 Marlon Brando, Eva Marie Saint	22. *On the Waterfront*
23.	1955 Ernest Borgnine, Betsy Blair	23. *Marty*
24.	1956 David Niven, Shirley MacLaine	24. *Around the World in Eighty Days*
25.	1957 William Holden, Alec Guinness	25. *The Bridge on the River Kwai*
26.	1952 Betty Hutton, Charlton Heston	26. *The Greatest Show on Earth*
27.	1951 Gene Kelly, Leslie Caron	27. *An American in Paris*
28.	1950 Bette Davis, Anne Baxter	28. *All About Eve*
29.	1949 Broderick Crawford, Joanne Dru	29. *All the King's Men*
30.	1948 Laurence Olivier, Eileen Herlie	30. *Hamlet*

OSCARS: BEST ACTOR AWARD

Given the name of the best actor and the year for which he won the Oscar, name the movie.

Freshman Level

1. 1976 Peter Finch
2. 1970 George C. Scott
3. 1978 Jon Voight
4. 1972 Marlon Brando
5. 1952 Gary Cooper
6. 1944 Bing Crosby
7. 1951 Humphrey Bogart
8. 1955 Ernest Borgnine
9. 1956 Yul Bryner
10. 1960 Burt Lancaster

1. *Network*
2. *Patton*
3. *Coming Home*
4. *The Godfather*
5. *High Noon*
6. *Going My Way*
7. *The African Queen*
8. *Marty*
9. *The King and I*
10. *Elmer Gantry*

Graduate Level

11. 1946 Fredric March
12. 1969 John Wayne
13. 1977 Richard Dreyfuss
14. 1953 William Holden
15. 1962 Gregory Peck
16. 1967 Rod Steiger
17. 1965 Lee Marvin
18. 1968 Cliff Robertson
19. 1941 Gary Cooper
20. 1960 Burt Lancaster

11. *The Best Years of Our Lives*
12. *True Grit*
13. *The Goodbye Girl*
14. *Stalag 17*
15. *To Kill a Mockingbird*
16. *In the Heat of the Night*
17. *Cat Ballou*
18. *Charly*
19. *Sergeant York*
20. *Elmer Gantry*

Ph.D. Level

21. 1943 Paul Lukas
22. 1958 David Niven
23. 1961 Maximillian Schell
24. 1938 Spencer Tracy
25. 1973 Jack Lemmon
26. 1974 Art Carney
27. 1935 Victor McLaglen
28. 1947 Ronald Colman
29. 1945 Ray Milland
30. 1940 James Stewart

21. *Watch on the Rhine*
22. *Separate Tables*
23. *Judgment at Nuremberg*
24. *Boys Town*
25. *Save the Tiger*
26. *Harry and Tonto*
27. *The Informer*
28. *A Double Life*
29. *The Lost Weekend*
30. *The Philadelphia Story*

OSCARS: BEST ACTRESS AWARD

Given the name of the best actress and the year for which she won the Oscar, name the movie.

Freshman Level

1. 1978 Jane Fonda
2. 1962 Anne Bancroft
3. 1964 Julie Andrews
4. 1976 Faye Dunaway
5. 1972 Liza Minnelli
6. 1958 Susan Hayward
7. 1971 Jane Fonda
8. 1945 Joan Crawford
9. 1960 Elizabeth Taylor
10. 1973 Glenda Jackson

1. *Coming Home*
2. *The Miracle Worker*
3. *Mary Poppins*
4. *Network*
5. *Cabaret*
6. *I Want to Live*
7. *Klute*
8. *Mildred Pierce*
9. *Butterfield 8*
10. *A Touch of Class*

Graduate Level

11. 1954 Grace Kelly
12. 1961 Sophia Loren
13. 1967 Katharine Hepburn
14. 1965 Julie Christie
15. 1956 Ingrid Bergman
16. 1951 Vivien Leigh
17. 1939 Vivian Leigh
18. 1948 Jane Wyman
19. 1952 Shirley Booth
20. 1969 Maggie Smith

11. *The Country Girl*
12. *Two Women*
13. *Guess Who's Coming to Dinner*
14. *Darling*
15. *Anastasia*
16. *A Streetcar Named Desire*
17. *Gone With the Wind*
18. *Johnny Belinda*
19. *Come Back Little Sheba*
20. *The Prime of Miss Jean Brodie*

Ph.D. Level

21. 1974 Ellen Burstyn
22. 1970 Glenda Jackson
23. 1929 Mary Pickford
24. 1959 Simone Signoret
25. 1957 Joanne Woodward
26. 1953 Audrey Hepburn
27. 1950 Judy Holliday
28. 1933 Katharine Hepburn
29. 1935 Bette Davis
30. 1934 Claudette Colbert

21. *Alice Doesn't Live Here Anymore*
22. *Women in Love*
23. *Coquette*
24. *Room at the Top*
25. *The Three Faces of Eve*
26. *Roman Holiday*
27. *Born Yesterday*
28. *Morning Glory*
29. *Dangerous*
30. *It Happened One Night*

CLASSICS: MOVIES

Freshman Level

All questions deal with the movie *The Wizard of Oz*.

1. What was the name of Dorothy's dog?
2. Name two of the three things which the wizard awarded to Dorothy's friends.
3. Who portrayed the Wizard?
4. Who portrayed the Scarecrow?
5. Who portrayed the Tin Man?
6. Who portrayed the Lion?
7. What role did Billie Burke portray?
8. Which major Oscar did the film win?
9. Where did the Wizard live?
10. Although nominated for best picture, it lost to . . .

1. Toto
2. Diploma, medal, testimonial
3. Frank Morgan
4. Ray Bolger
5. Jack Haley
6. Bert Lahr
7. Glinda
8. Best song
9. Emerald City
10. *Gone with the Wind*

Graduate Level

All questions deal with the movie *The Grapes of Wrath*.

11. From which state did the family come?
12. What was the family's last name?
13. What was the first name of the character portrayed by Henry Fonda?
14. Who portrayed Ma?
15. The director won an Oscar. He was . . .
16. What other major Oscar did the film win?

17. What fruit were the workers being paid to pick?
18. Who portrayed the defrocked preacher, Casy?
19. ". . . any fella that wants thirty cents an hour when I'm payin' twenty-five". This was Mr. King's definition of a . . .
20. What was Gregg Toland's contribution to the film?

11. Oklahoma
12. Joad
13. Tom

14. Jane Darwell
15. John Ford
16. Best Supporting Actress

17. Peaches
18. John Carradine
19. Red (communist)

20. Photography

Ph.D. Level

All questions deal with the movie *King's Row*.

21. What role did Robert Cummings portray?
22. Who portrayed Drake McHugh?
23. Who portrayed Dr. Alexander Tower?
24. Dr. Tower's daughter was portrayed by Betty Field. What was the daughter's name?
25. Who portrayed the sadistic Dr. Henry Gordon?
26. The title of Ronald Reagan's autobiography is a line from *King's Row*. It is . . .
27. What eventually happened to Dr. Tower's daughter?
28. To what distant city did Parris travel?
29. Who portrayed Drake's faithful girlfriend, Randy Monaghan?
30. What role was played by Judith Anderson?

21. Parris Mitchell
22. Ronald Reagan
23. Claude Rains
24. Cassandra

25. Charles Coburn
26. *Where's the Rest of Me?*

27. He poisoned her
28. Vienna
29. Ann Sheridan
30. Mrs. Harriet Gordon

EPIC FILMS

Freshman Level

1. Marlon Brando plays Fletcher Christian.
2. Karl Malden plays General Bradley.
3. Charles Laughton plays Quasimodo.

4. Fay Wray plays Anne Darrow.
5. John Wayne plays Davey Crockett and Richard Widmark plays Jim Bowie.
6. David Niven plays Phileas Fogg and Shirley MacLaine plays Princess Aouda.
7. Michael Parks plays Adam and Richard Harris plays Cain.
8. Charles Laughton plays Captain Bligh.
9. Richard Burton as Antony and Rex Harrison as Caesar.
10. Leslie Howard plays Ashley Wilkes.

1. *Mutiny on the Bounty*
2. *Patton*
3. *The Hunchback of Notre Dame*
4. *King Kong*
5. *The Alamo*
6. *Around the World in Eighty Days*
7. *The Bible*
8. *Mutiny on the Bounty*
9. *Cleopatra*
10. *Gone With the Wind*

Graduate Level

11. H. B. Warner as Jesus and Dorothy Cumming as Mary.
12. Gregory Peck as Mallory and David Niven as Miller.
13. Lew Ayres plays Paul Baumer.

14. William Holden plays Shears and Alec Guinness plays Colonel Nicholson.
15. Jean Simmons as Merit and Victor Mature as Horemheb.
16. Rock Hudson as Bick Benedict and James Dean as Jett Rink.
17. Dorothy McGuire as Mary and Charlton Heston as John the Baptist.
18. Betty Hutton as Holly and Cornel Wilde as Sebastian.

19. Ronald Colman as Robert Conway and Jane Wyatt as Sandra.
20. Peter Ustinov as Nero.

11. *King of Kings*
12. *The Guns of Navarone*
13. *All Quiet on the Western Front*
14. *The Bridge on the River Kwai*
15. *The Egyptian*
16. *Giant*
17. *The Greatest Story Ever Told*
18. *The Greatest Show on Earth*
19. *Lost Horizon*
20. *Quo Vadis*

Ph.D. Level

21. Charlton Heston as Michelangelo and Rex Harrison as the Pope.
22. Trevor Howard as Lord Cardigan and Vanessa Redgrave as Clarissa.
23. Jennifer Jones as Pearl Chavez and Herbert Marshall as Scott Chavez.
24. Paul Newman as Ari Ben Canaan and Eva Marie Saint as Kitty Fremont.
25. Spencer Tracy as Major Rogers and Robert Young as Langdon Towne.
26. Henry Fonda as Pierre Bezukhov and Audrey Hepburn as Natasha.
27. Keir Dullea as Bowman.
28. Kirk Douglas as Einar and Tony Curtis as Eric.
29. Clara Bow as Mary Preston and Charles Rogers as Jack Powell.
30. Ray Milland as Stephen Tolliver and Paulette Goddard as Loxi Clairborne.

21. *The Agony and the Ecstasy*
22. *The Charge of the Light Brigade*
23. *Duel in the Sun*
24. *Exodus*
25. *Northwest Passage*
26. *War and Peace*
27. *2001: A Space Odyssey*
28. *The Vikings*
29. *Wings*
30. *Reap the Wild Wind*

MOVIE PLOTS

Freshman Level

1. The migration of poor workers from the dust bowl to the California fruit valleys.
2. A very successful romance about the American Civil War.
3. Hollywood's most successful retelling of a fairy story.
4. A modern naval story involving a paranoiac, Captain Queeg.
5. A tale of two young motorcyclists traveling across America.
6. A good location thriller about the docks protection rackets.
7. Disney's ambitious concert sequence of cartoons.
8. A marathon film about the birth of Israel, starring Paul Newman.
9. Supernatural horror piece about a young girl possessed by a devil.
10. Hemingway's tough romantic anti-war novel.

1. *The Grapes of Wrath*
2. *Gone With the Wind*
3. *The Wizard of Oz*
4. *The Caine Mutiny*
5. *Easy Rider*
6. *On the Waterfront*
7. *Fantasia*
8. *Exodus*
9. *The Exorcist*
10. *A Farewell to Arms*

Graduate Level

11. A striking musical about Berlin in the 1930s.
12. Harold Robbins's story had George Peppard as a Howard Hughes-type mogul.
13. This melodrama immortalized Dooley Wilson singing "As Time Goes By".
14. A society where books are outlawed and firemen start fires.
15. The first internationally successful "spaghetti western".
16. An American, living with guerrillas during the Spanish Civil War, sacrifices his life for their cause.
17. A classic film about a huge gorilla.
18. The rise to fame of an unscrupulous actress, starring Bette Davis.
19. An old-time revivalist religion film starring Burt Lancaster.
20. The celebrated confrontation between Wyatt Earp and the Clanton Gang.

11. *Cabaret*
12. *The Carpetbaggers*
13. *Casablanca*
14. *Fahrenheit 451*
15. *A Fistful of Dollars*
16. *For Whom the Bell Tolls*
17. *King Kong*
18. *All About Eve*
19. *Elmer Gantry*
20. *The Gunfight at the O.K. Corral*

Ph.D. Level

21. James Fenimore Cooper's adventure novel of American colonization.
22. A Hitchcock movie notable for confining itself to the smallest acting space of any film ever made.
23. A thriller set in war-torn Vienna featuring zither music.
24. About the court of Henry II (Katharine Hepburn won an Oscar).
25. An old-fashioned back-stage story with "Eternally" as the theme.
26. Alec Guinness and his gang move in on a little old lady who innocently brings about their doom.
27. About a missing gem, a debt of honor, and savagery in the Foreign Legion.
28. A James Stewart western with Jeff Chandler as Cochise.
29. A brief romance between two married peole who meet in a train station cafe.
30. A one-armed stranger defies violence to prove the townsfolk were guilty of an old murder.

21. *The Last of the Mohicans*
22. *Lifeboat*
23. *The Third Man*
24. *The Lion in Winter*
25. *Limelight*
26. *The Lady Killers*
27. *Beau Geste*
28. *Broken Arrow*
29. *Brief Encounter*
30. *Bad Day at Black Rock*

TELEVISION: QUOTATIONS
Identify the name of the show on which each expression might be heard.

Freshman Level

1. "Verry eent'restink"

2. "Would you believe?"
3. "To the moon, Alice"
4. "Sit on it."
5. "Smile, you're on . . ."
6. "Na nu, na nu."
7. "Meathead" and "Dingbat."
8. "Yabba dabba doo."
9. "Just the facts, ma'am."
10. "Phasers on stun."

1. *Rowan and Martin's Laugh-In*
2. *Get Smart*
3. *The Honeymooners*
4. *Happy Days*
5. *Candid Camera*
6. *Mork and Mindy*
7. *All in the Family*
8. *The Flintstones*
9. *Dragnet*
10. *Star Trek*

Graduate Level

11. "Dy-No-Mite."
12. "This is the dimension of imagination."
13. "Well, I'll be a dirty bird!"
14. "God'll get you for that."
15. "Uh-one, uh-two"

16. "Boss, the plane!"
17. "C'mon down!"
18. "Kiss my grits."
19. "Coming Mother!"
20. "This tape will self-destruct in five seconds."

11. *Good Times*
12. *The Twilight Zone*
13. *The George Gobel Show*
14. *Maude*
14. *The Lawrence Welk Show*
16. *Fantasy Island*
17. *The Price is Right*
18. *Alice and/or Flo*
19. *The Aldrich Family*
20. *Mission Impossible*

Ph.D. Level

21. "Cosmic Cow"
22. "Whatchoo talkin about?"
23. "But most of all, I remember. . ."
24. "There you go."
25. "Good evening. I'm____and you're not."
26. "Grease for Peace."
27. "Till then. . .try dancing."

28. "History as she ain't."
29. "That's three down and seven to go. Mr. Cerf?"
30. "Pigs in Space."

21. *Too Close for Comfort*
22. *Diff'rent Strokes*
23. *Mama*
24. *McCloud*
25. *Saturday Night Live*
26. *Sha Na Na*
27. *The Arthur Murray Show*
28. *Your Show of Shows*
29. *What's My Line*
30. *The Muppet Show*

STARS AND THEIR FILMS
Name the actor/actress who has played in all three of the films named.

Freshman Level

1. *Elephant Walk, Doctor Faustus, The Sandpiper.*
2. *Guys and Dolls, One Eyed Jacks, The Young Lions.*
3. *Stage Door, The Lion in Winter, The Philadelphia Story.*
4. *Cactus Flower, Shampoo, There's a Girl in My Soup.*
5. *Blithe Spirit, My Fair Lady, Major Barbara.*
6. *North by Northwest, An Affair to Remember, Indiscreet.*
7. *Straw Dogs, Midnight Cowboy, The Graduate.*
8. *Picnic, The Wild Bunch, Sunset Boulevard.*
9. *The Misfits, Niagara, The Asphalt Jungle.*
10. *Judge Roy Bean, The Prize, Harper.*

1. Elizabeth Taylor
2. Marlon Brando
3. Katharine Hepburn
4. Goldie Hawn
5. Rex Harrison
6. Cary Grant
7. Dustin Hoffman
8. William Holden
9. Marilyn Monroe
10. Paul Newman

Graduate Level

11. *Ivanhoe, Quo Vadis, Waterloo Bridge.*
12. *Wives and Lovers, The Caine Mutiny, Miracle in the Rain.*
13. *Ben Hur, Lawrence of Arabia, The Cruel Sea.*
14. *How to Marry a Millionaire, Coney Island, The Gay Divorcee.*
15. *The Carpetbaggers, The Big Land, Shane.*
16. *Home from the Hill, Jack of Diamonds, Once is Not Enough.*
17. *The Last Safari, Beau Brummel, Scaramouche.*
18. *Cover Girl, Pal Joey, Separate Tables.*
19. *The Music Box, Blockheads, Babes in Toyland.*
20. *Johnny Belinda, The Big Country, Of Mice and Men.*

11. Robert Taylor
12. Van Johnson
13. Jack Hawkins
14. Betty Grable
15. Alan Ladd
16. George Hamilton
17. Stewart Granger
18. Rita Hayworth
19. Oliver Hardy and/or Stan Laurel
20. Charles Bickford

Ph.D. Level

21. *Kentucky, Come and Get It, Rio Bravo.*
22. *Gone With the Wind, The Scarlet Pimpernel, Of Human Bondage.*
23. *The Desert Fox, The Winslow Boy, King Solomon's Mines.*
24. *Farewell My Lovely, The Sundowners, Ryan's Daughter.*
25. *The Wrong Box, Ryan's Daughter, Tunes of Glory.*
26. *Dial M for Murder, Beau Geste, The Lost Weekend.*
27. *After the Fox, The Egyptian, The Robe.*
28. *Ryan's Daughter, Mutiny on the Bounty, Brief Encounter.*
29. *Attack, The Killers, Cat Ballou.*
30. *Nothing Sacred, Executive Suite, Inherit the Wind.*

21. Walter Brennan
22. Leslie Howard
23. Sir Cedric Hardwicke
24. Robert Mitchum
25. John Mills
26. Ray Milland
27. Victor Mature
28. Trevor Howard
29. Lee Marvin
30. Fredric March

TELEVISION: CHARACTERS

Name the show in which the given character appears.

Freshman Level

1. Murray the cop
2. Endora
3. Brenda Morgenstern
4. Sweathogs
5. Dr. Robert Hartley
6. Schneider
7. Gopher
8. Opie Taylor
9. Laura Petrie
10. Tattoo

1. *The Odd Couple*
2. *Bewitched*
3. *Rhoda*
4. *Welcome Back Kotter*
5. *The Bob Newhart Show*
6. *One Day at a Time*
7. *The Love Boat*
8. *The Andy Griffith Show*
9. *The Dick Van Dyke Show*
10. *Fantasy Island*

Graduate Level

11. Orson
12. Venus Flytrap
13. Reverend Jim
14. Dr. Zorba
15. District Attorney Hamilton Burger
16. Mrs. Carmichael
17. Grandpa Amos
18. Lily Ruskin
19. Aunt Esther Anderson
20. Governor Gatling

11. *Mork and Mindy*
12. *WKRP in Cincinnati*
13. *Taxi*
14. *Ben Casey*
15. *Perry Mason*
16. *The Lucy Show*
17. *The Real McCoys*
18. *December Bride*
19. *Sanford and Son*
20. *Benson*

Ph.D. Level

21. Ralph Furley
22. Peter Campbell
23. Mr. French
24. Officer Ed Wells
25. Sgt. Suzanne Anderson
26. Huggy Bear
27. Angel Martin
28. Officer Barickza
29. Janet Wood
30. Bruno Martelli

21. *Three's Company*
22. *Soap*
23. *Family Affair*
24. *Adam 12*
25. *Police Woman*
26. *Starsky and Hutch*
27. *The Rockford Files*
28. *CHiPs*
29. *Three's Company*
30. *Fame*

FILMS WITH COLORS IN THE TITLE

Fill in the color that is missing from each movie title.

Freshman Level

1. *The Corn Is _____*
2. *_____ Beauty*
3. *The _____ Berets*
4. *The _____ Panther*
5. *Wake of the _____ Witch*
6. *The _____ Stallion*
7. *The _____ Max*
8. *_____ Friday*
9. *_____ Hawaii*
10. *The _____ Submarine*

1. *Green*
2. *Black*
3. *Green*
4. *Pink*
5. *Red*
6. *Black*
7. *Blue*
8. *Black*
9. *Blue*
10. *Yellow*

Graduate Level

11. *The _____ Pimpernel*
12. *The _____ Balloon*
13. *The Moon Is _____*
14. *The Man in _____*
15. *How _____ Was My Valley*
16. *Bad Day at _____ Rock*
17. *Clockwork _____*
18. *Ruggles of _____ Gap*
19. *Riders of the _____ Sage*
20. *Last of the _____ Hot Lovers*

11. *Scarlet*
12. *Red*
13. *Blue*
14. *Grey*
15. *Green*
16. *Black*
17. *Orange*
18. *Red*
19. *Purple*
20. *Red*

Ph.D. Level

21. *The _____ Angel*
22. *_____ Heat*
23. *The _____ Knight*
24. *The Creature from the _____ Lagoon*
25. *The _____ Rolls-Royce*
26. *A Patch of _____*
27. *_____ Ball Express*
28. *Forever _____*
29. *_____ Feather*
30. *The _____ Gardenia*

21. *Blue*
22. *White*
23. *Blue*
24. *Black*
25. *Yellow*
26. *Blue*
27. *Red*
28. *Amber*
29. *White*
30. *Blue*

TWISTED TELEVISION PROGRAMS

One letter in each title has been changed. Correct the title.

Freshman Level

1. The Frying Nun
2. Sanford and Ron
3. Happy Ways
4. My Three Sins
5. The Old Couple
6. Cheeks
7. What's My Fine?
8. Adam's Bib
9. Kodak
10. Little Horse On The Prairie

1. *The Flying Nun*
2. *Sanford and Son*
3. *Happy Days*
4. *My Three Sons*
5. *The Odd Couple*
6. *Cheers*
7. *What's My Line?*
8. *Adam's Rib*
9. *Kojak*
10. *Little House On The Prairie*

Graduate Level

11. Have Fun Will Travel
12. One Way at a Time
13. Falcon Crust
14. Moonsighting
15. You Bet Your Wife
16. The Mud Squad
17. Food Times
18. The Price Is Light
19. Bet Smart
20. Your Hat Parade

11. *Have Gun Will Travel*
12. *One Day at a Time*
13. *Falcon Crest*
14. *Moonlighting*
15. *You Bet Your Life*
16. *The Mod Squad*
17. *Good Times*
18. *The Price Is Right*
19. *Get Smart*
20. *Your Hit Parade*

Ph. D. Level

21. Slipper
22. Growing Pawns
23. Wagon Trail
24. The Lone Boat
25. December Pride
26. The Tall Guy
27. Soup
28. Bag Town
29. Light Is Enough
30. House Walls

21. *Flipper*
22. *Growing Pains*
23. *Wagon Train*
24. *The Love Boat*
25. *December Bride*
26. *The Fall Guy*
27. *Soap*
28. *Big Town*
29. *Eight Is Enough*
30. *House Calls*

FILMS WITH NUMBERS IN THE TITLE

Fill in the number that is missing from each movie title

Freshman Level

1. Ali Baba and the _____ Thieves
2. Catch-_____
3. Around the World in _____ Days
4. _____ Star Final
5. The Magnificent _____
6. Miracle on _____ Street
7. Under _____ Flags
8. _____ : A Space Odyssey
9. _____ O'Clock High
10. The _____ Commandments

1. Forty
2. 22
3. Eighty
4. Five
5. Seven
6. 34th
7. Two
8. 2001
9. Twelve
10. Ten

Graduate Level

11. _____ Dalmatians
12. North Dallas _____
13. Ceiling _____
14. Butterfield _____
15. The _____ Chairs
16. _____ Leagues Under the Sea
17. _____ Years Before the Mast
18. The Wild _____
19. The _____ Year Itch
20. _____ Coins in the Fountain

11. 101
12. 40
13. Zero
14. 8
15. Twelve
16. Twenty Thousand
17. Two
18. One
19. Seven
20. Three

Ph.D. Level

21. Fahrenheit _____
22. The _____ Steps
23. _____ Seconds Over Tokyo
24. _____ Days at Peking
25. The _____ Foot Bride of Candy Rock
26. _____ Mules for Sister Sara
27. _____ Days of the Condor
28. _____ Easy Pieces
29. _____ North Frederick
30. Slaughterhouse _____

21. 451
22. Thirty Nine
23. Thirty
24. 55
25. 30
26. Two
27. Three
28. Five
29. Ten
30. Five

TELEVISION: THEME SONGS
Identify the TV program from the given theme.

Freshman Level

1. "Moving on UP"
2. "Those Were the Days"
3. "The Ballad of Jed Clampett"
4. "Danny Boy"
5. "When You Wish Upon a Star"
6. "Moon River"
7. "See the U.S.A. in your Chevrolet"
8. "Johnny's Theme"
9. "Welcome Back"
10. "Dream Along with Me"

1. *The Jeffersons*
2. *All in the Family*
3. *The Beverly Hillbillies*
4. *The Danny Thomas Show*
5. *Walt Disney*
6. *The Andy Williams Show*
7. *The Dinah Shore Chevy Show*
8. *The Tonight Show Starring Johnny Carson*
9. *Welcome Back Kotter*
10. *The Perry Como Show*

Graduate Level

11. "The Ballad of Paladin"
12. "Keep Your Eye on the Sparrow"
13. "There's a New Girl in Town"
14. "Making Our Dreams Come True"
15. "Rock Around the Clock"
16. "Sing Along"
17. "Believe It or Not"
18. Theme based on "Funeral March of a Marionette"
19. "Bubbles in the Wine"
20. "Love in Bloom"

11. *Have Gun Will Travel*
12. *Baretta*
13. *Alice*
14. *Laverne and Shirley*
15. *Happy Days*
16. *Sing Along with Mitch*
17. *The Greatest American Hero*
18. *Alfred Hitchcock Presents*
19. *The Lawrence Welk Show*
20. *The Jack Benny Show*

Ph.D. Level

21. "Near You"
22. "If I Could Tell You"
23. "The Bell Waltz"
24. "The First Years"
25. "Lucky Day"
26. "I'm Getting Sentimental Over You"
27. "Happy Days"
28. "Danger Ahead"
29. "Gobelues"
30. "The Perfect Song"

21. *The Milton Berle Show*
22. *The Voice of Firestone*
23. *The Bell Telephone Hour*
24. *The Paper Chase*
25. *Your Hit Parade*
26. *Stage Door*
27. *The Donna Reed Show*
28. *Dragnet*
29. *The George Gobel Show*
30. *Amos 'n' Andy*

CLASSIC MOVIES

Freshman Level

All questions deal with the movie *Casablanca* (1942).

1. He played the prefect of police, Captain Louis Renault.
2. The destination of the plane at the end of the film.
3. He played the role of Richard Blaine.
4. What was the name of the piano player at Rick's Place?
5. Ugarte killed two German couriers and was arrested in "Rick's place." Who portrayed Ugarte?
6. The Germans wanted to arrest Victor Laszlo for allegedly publishing lies. Who played Victor?
7. Ilsa Lund said, "Play it, Sam." What was "it"?
8. Where were the letters of transit hidden?
9. Ferrari buys Rick's place. Who played Ferrari?
10. Ilsa didn't meet Rick, as promised, at the train station because she received what news?

1. Claude Rains
2. Lisbon
3. Humphrey Bogart
4. Sam
5. Peter Lorre
6. Paul Henreid
7. "As Time Goes By"
8. In Sam's piano
9. Sidney Greenstreet
10. Her husband was alive

Graduate Level

All questions deal with the movie *Gone With the Wind* (1939).

11. What was the name of the O'Hara plantation?
12. Who played Scarlett O'Hara?
13. Who played Melanie Hamilton?
14. Who played Prissy?
15. Who produced the movie?
16. What are the first spoken words in the film?
17. What is the closing line?

18. What was the name of Ashley Wilkes's plantation?
19. Scarlett regains her wealth by investing in what type of business?
20. What does the movie have in common with these movies: *The Wizard of Oz*, *Wuthering Heights*, and *Goodbye Mr. Chips*?

11. Tara
12. Vivien Leigh
13. Olivia de Havilland
14. Butterfly McQueen
15. David O. Selznick
16. "Quittin' time."
17. "After all, tomorrow is another day."
18. Twelve Oaks
19. A sawmill
20. All were nominated for best picture in 1939.

Ph.D. Level

All questions deal with the movie *Citizen Kane* (1941).

21. What was Kane's full name?
22. Who played Kane's mother?
23. Kane's second wife had what profession at the time of their marriage?
24. Kane's best friend, Jedediah Leland, was played by . . .
25. The movie script paralleled the career of this newspaper magnate.
26. What was the name of Kane's mansion?
27. This was the name of Welles's company of theater actors.
28. Kane's mansion was modeled after the mansion located at . . .
29. What was Kane's dying word?
30. What or whom did it refer to?

21. Charles Foster Kane
22. Agnes Moorehead
23. Singer
24. Joseph Cotten
25. William Randolph Hearst
26. Xanadu
27. Mercury Theatre
28. San Simeon, Calif.
29. "Rosebud."
30. Kane's sled as a child

MUSIC: THE BEATLES, SONG TITLES RECORDED
Complete the song title by providing the last word.

Freshman Level

1. "All You Need Is . . .
2. "A Hard Day's . . .
3. "Don't Let Me . . .
4. "Yellow . . .
5. "Can't Buy Me . . .
6. "Twist and . . .
7. "Lucy in the Sky with . . .
8. "Strawberry . . .
9. "It Won't Be . . .
10. "Let It . . .

1. Love"
2. Night"
3. Down"
4. Submarine"
5. Love"
6. Shout"
7. Diamonds"
8. Fields"
9. Long"
10. Be"

Graduate Level

11. "Love Me . . .
12. "Lady . . .
13. "A Day in the . . .
14. "Get . . .
15. "Paperback . . .
16. "I Should Have Known . . .
17. "Ticket to . . .
18. "I Saw Her Standing . . .
19. "We Can Work It . . .
20. "With a Little Help from My . . .

11. Do"
12. Madonna"
13. Life"
14. Back"
15. Writer
16. Better"
17. Ride"
18. There"
19. Out"
20. Friends"

Ph.D. Level

21. "I Am the . . .
22. "Day . . .
23. "Rocky . . .
24. "Do You Want to Know a . . .
25. "Sexy . . .
26. "Back in the . . .
27. "Honey . . .
28. "Got to Get You into My . . .
29. "World Without . . .
30. "Helter . . .

21. Walrus"
22. Tripper"
23. Raccoon"
24. Secret?"
25. Sadie"
26. U.S.S.R."
27. Pie"
28. Life"
29. Love"
30. Skelter"

THE STAGE

Freshman Level

1. This musical comedy was based on a comic strip about a curly-haired girl and her dog.
2. In this play Richard Kiley starred as Don Quixote.
3. This Neil Simon play takes place in suites 203 and 204 of the Beverly Hills Motel.
4. This 1975 musical focuses on the unrecognized dancers of the Broadway theater scene.
5. Tennessee Williams won a Pulitzer Prize in 1955 for . . .
6. Doris and George, both married, meet once a year to make love.
7. This play ends with, "Captain, this is Ensign Pulver. I just threw your palm tree overboard."
8. This play is about a salesman named Willy Loman.
9. This musical contains the song "Getting to Know You"
10. Who portrayed the title role in *The King and I*?

1. *Annie*
2. *Man of La Mancha*
3. *California Suite*
4. *A Chorus Line*
5. *Cat on a Hot Tin Roof*
6. *Same Time Next Year*
7. *Mister Roberts*
8. *Death of a Salesman*
9. *The King and I*
10. Yul Brynner

Graduate Level

11. The hit song "I Don't Know How to Love Him" is from . . .
12. Name another musical play about Jesus, which opened on Broadway in 1976.
13. This play was based on the life of a female Israeli leader.
14. Who portrayed the title role in *Mister Roberts*?
15. The closing line of the musical is "Eliza? Where the Devil are my slippers?"
16. Who portrayed Mark Twain in *Mark Twain Tonight*?
17. The musical based on Thornton Wilder's play *The Matchmaker*.
18. On Broadway who portrayed Dolly (1964)?
19. This play probes the mind of a young stable boy who is in love with horses.
20. What is the popular name of Broadway's Antoinette Perry Award?

11. *Jesus Christ Superstar*
12. *Godspell*
13. *Golda*
14. Henry Fonda
15. *My Fair Lady*
16. Hal Holbrook
17. *Hello, Dolly!*
18. Carol Channing
19. *Equus*
20. Tony

Ph.D. Level

21. The characters in this musical include Nathan Detroit, Rusty Charlie, and Benny Southstreet.
22. What is the occupation of the character named Sarah Brown in *Guys and Dolls*?
23. This Tennessee Williams play is set in a Bohemian hotel on Mexico's west coast.
24. Songs from this 1978 musical include "Honeysuckle Rose" and "It's a Sin to Tell a Lie."
25. This play, set in a mythical Grover's Corners, New Hampshire, won the Pulitzer Prize in 1938.
26. Who wrote the play *Our Town*?
27. In this play Sidney Bruhl is a burnt-out writer for Broadway.
28. In this musical the audience enters to find a banner proclaiming "Welcome Back Rydell Class of 1959."
29. Who wrote *The Iceman Cometh*?
30. What musical featured the song "Mack the Knife"?

21. *Guys and Dolls*
22. Salvation Army Officer
23. *The Night of the Iguana*
24. *Ain't Misbehavin'*
25. *Our Town*
26. Thornton Wilder
27. *Deathtrap*
28. *Grease*
29. Eugene O'Neill
30. *Threepenny Opera*

TELEVISION ROLES
Name the actor/actress who played the role.

Freshman Level

1. Vinnie Barbarino on *Welcome Back Kotter*
2. Arthur Fonzarelli on *Happy Days*
3. Bruce Wayne on *Batman*
4. Ken Hutchinson on *Starsky and Hutch*
5. John Boy Walton on *The Waltons*
6. Emily Hartley on *The Bob Newhart Show*
7. Major Margaret Houlihan on *M*A*S*H*
8. James Evans, Jr., on *Good Times*
9. Mike Stivic on *All in the Family*
10. Ed Norton on *The Honeymooners*

1. John Travolta
2. Henry Winkler
3. Adam West
4. David Soul
5. Richard Thomas
6. Suzanne Pleshette
7. Loretta Swit
8. Jimmie Walker
9. Rob Reiner
10. Art Carney

Graduate Level

11. Barbara Cooper on *One Day at a Time*
12. Kris Monroe on *Charlie's Angels*
13. Lisa Douglas on *Green Acres*
14. Jed Clampett on *The Beverly Hillbillies*
15. Steve Douglas on *My Three Sons*
16. Sgt. Joe Friday on *Dragnet*
17. Richard Kimble on *The Fugitive*
18. Connie Brooks on *Our Miss Brooks*
19. Ted Baxter on *The Mary Tyler Moore Show*
20. Murray Slaughter on *The Mary Tyler Moore show*

11. Valerie Bertinelli
12. Cheryl Ladd
13. Eva Gabor
14. Buddy Ebson
15. Fred MacMurray
16. Jack Webb
17. David Janssen
18. Eve Arden
19. Ted Knight
20. Gavin MacLeod

Ph.D. Level

21. Rudy Jordache on *Rich Man, Poor Man*
22. Oliver Wendell Douglas on *Green Acres*
23. Agent 99 on *Get Smart*
24. Peter Newkirk on *Hogan's Heroes*
25. Ginger Grant on *Gilligan's Island*
26. Constance Mackenzie on *Peyton Place*
27. Endorra on *Bewitched*
28. Osgood Conklin on *Our Miss Brooks*
29. Chester Riley on *The Life of Riley*
30. Lily Ruskin on *December Bride*

21. Peter Strauss
22. Eddie Albert
23. Barbara Feldon
24. Richard Dawson
25. Tina Louise
26. Dorothy Malone
27. Agnes Moorehead
28. Gale Gordon
29. William Bendix
30. Spring Byington

MUSIC: ELVIS

Freshman Level

1. This was his first film.
2. He said, "I basically became a musician because of Elvis Presley."
3. In 1955, this man started to represent Elvis exclusively.
4. Name the song "Well, they said you was high class, well that was just a lie."
5. He said Presley would never appear on his show.
6. Where was Elvis from 1958 to 1960?
7. This was the name of his Memphis mansion.
8. He married her in 1967.
9. This song was on the flip side of the 78 rpm and 45 rpm single "Hound Dog."
10. This song, first recorded by Al Jolson, appears on several Elvis albums.

1. *Love Me Tender*
2. John Lennon
3. Colonel Tom Parker
4. "Hound Dog"
5. Ed Sullivan
6. U.S. Army
7. Graceland
8. Priscilla Beaulieu
9. "Don't Be Cruel"
10. "Are You Lonesome Tonight?"

Graduate Level

11. He said, "Elvis recorded a song of mine. That's the one recording I treasure most."
12. This 1961 film was his most successful.
13. Of all his songs, this was reputedly Elvis' favorite.
14. This 1972 documentary was his final film.
15. She is Elvis and Priscilla's daughter.
16. Who was Jesse Garon Presley?

17. When Elvis first appeared here, he was advised to go back to truck driving.
18. This label was the first to record Elvis.
19. She co-starred with Elvis in *Viva Las Vegas*
20. When Elvis went to Europe in 1958, he said, "The first place I want to go is Paris and look up . . ."

11. Bob Dylan
12. *Blue Hawaii*
13. "It's Now or Never"
14. *Elvis on Tour*
15. Lisa
16. Twin brother (died at birth)
17. Grand Ole Opry
18. Sun Records
19. Ann-Margret
20. Brigitte Bardot

Ph.D. Level

21. What was Elvis first known as?
22. In this movie Elvis played opposite Mary Tyler Moore.
23. He wrote "Don't Be Cruel" and "All Shook Up" for Elvis.
24. This was his first release after coming out of the army.
25. This 1970 film is a documentary of his Vegas act.

26. This 1968 film co-starred Nancy Sinatra and Bill Bixby.
27. He was Elvis' original guitarist in Memphis.
28. In 1955 this song went to number one on the country and western chart.
29. What are these: Red Eagle, Mad Tiger, and Peacock?
30. He said, ". . . I thank God for Elvis Presley."

21. The Hillbilly Cat
22. *Change of Habit*
23. Otis Blackwell
24. "Stuck on You"
25. *Elvis: That's the Way It Is*
26. *Speedway*
27. Scotty Moore
28. "Mystery Train"
29. Concert jumpsuits
30. Little Richard

TELEVISION SERIES
Name the TV series from the plot description.

Freshman Level

1. To get rid of Darrin, Endora produces a double for Samantha.
2. Richie and Potsie pool their funds for a sporty convertible.
3. The girls fly to Hawaii to rescue kidnapped Charlie.
4. Bob offers advice on how to handle personal anger.
5. Ted surprises everyone with expensive gifts from his income tax return.
6. Hawkeye discovers why Charles is living the life of Riley.
7. Chrissy assumes Jack isn't getting enough affection when she learns he's seeing an older woman.
8. When Murray's wife ejects him, Felix invites him in.
9. The crew of the *Enterprise* is captured by Aliens.
10. Mike and Gloria plan to leave Joey with friends in the event of their deaths.

1. *Bewitched*
2. *Happy Days*
3. *Charlie's Angels*
4. *The Bob Newhart Show*
5. *The Mary Tyler Moore Show*
6. *M*A*S*H*
7. *Three's Company*
8. *The Odd Couple*
9. *Star Trek*
10. *All in the Family*

Graduate Level

11. A weekend at Exidor's cabin does not provide much rest.
12. Laura and Nellie battle for Almanzo's attention.
13. Relatives of a kidnapped VIP throw the 12th Precinct into chaos.
14. Jennifer finally accepts a date with Herb.
15. A bus tour guide falls in love with Mel and he turns his diner into a tourist attraction.
16. Fred dreams that Lamont is the "Spirit of Christmas."
17. McGarrett tries to find out why someone is murdering members of a birdwatching group.
18. Sue Ellen's baby is kidnapped.
19. A plump woman wanting to become slim visits the island.
20. While Grandpa visits a social worker Loretta cuts a record.

11. *Mork and Mindy*
12. *Little House on the Prairie*
13. *Barney Miller*
14. *WKRP in Cincinnati*
15. *Alice*
16. *Sanford and Son*
17. *Hawaii Five-O*
18. *Dallas*
19. *Fantasy Island*
20. *Mary Hartman, Mary Hartman*

Ph.D. Level

21. Captain Furillo tries to forget a romantic breakup.
22. A fatal fire poses a dilemma for the editors of the *Tribune*.
23. Jonathon and Jennifer track the killers of a chemist.
24. Banner tries to unite a teenager with her mother.
25. Pepper goes undercover to search for a psychotic strangler.
26. Joanie learns that Tom owns stock in a porno theater.
27. The Bellamy household is disrupted by the 1926 strike.
28. Constance Carlyle undergoes surgery after her fall.
29. A timid man disguises himself aboard the *Pacific Princess*.
30. Ann, Barbara, and Schneider are surprised when Julie returns unexpectedly.

21. *Hill Street Blues*
22. *Lou Grant*
23. *Hart to Hart*
24. *The Incredible Hulk*
25. *Police Woman*
26. *Eight Is Enough*
27. *Upstairs, Downstairs*
28. *Flamingo Road*
29. *The Love Boat*
30. *One Day at a Time*

MUSIC: THE ROLLING STONES

Freshman Level

1. Name the song "I met a gin-soaked barroom queen in Memphis."
2. This is the documentary about the Altamont Speedway Concert of 1969.
3. He replaced Brian Jones.
4. This famous songstress was Mick's girlfriend.
5. Name the song "Please allow me to introduce myself, I'm a man of wealth and taste."
6. This album was the Stones answer to *Sergeant Pepper's Lonely Heart's Club Band.*
7. This is the name of Mick and Bianca's daughter.
8. This double album came out in 1972
9. Mick sings this song about living in New York.
10. He replaced Mick Taylor.

1. "Honkey Tonk Woman"
2. "Gimme Shelter"
3. Mick Taylor
4. Marianne Faithful
5. "Sympathy for the Devil"
6. "Their Satanic Majesties Request"
7. Jade
8. *Exile on Main Street*
9. "Shattered"
10. Ron Wood

Graduate Level

11. This is Tony Sanchez' best-selling book on the Stones.
12. What did Mick study before becoming a rock idol?
13. What does Sanchez say the title "Brown Sugar" refers to?
14. Who was ". . . born in the crossfire of a hurricane"?
15. This was the first number one hit single.
16. In early 1963, who did they open for at London's Marquee Club?
17. Born in 1936, he is the eldest Stone.
18. Where was Brian Jones's body found?
19. In what song does Mick say his favorite flavor is "cherry-red"?
20. Who would "never say where she came from"?

11. *Up and Down with the Rolling Stones*
12. Economics
13. Crude heroin
14. Jumpin Jack Flash
15. "Satisfaction"
16. Alexis Korner
17. Bill Wyman
18. In a pool
19. "You Can't Always Get What You Want"
20. Ruby Tuesday

Ph.D. Level

21. Who was "Angie" written for?
22. In "Mother's Little Helper," what is a drag '?
23. They were hired for the security at Altamont.
24. The advertising for this album featured a woman bound and beaten.
25. In 1981, they went under this name when playing warm-up gigs.
26. This was the name of Ron and Keith's group at Knebworth in 1979.
27. Ron Wood came from this group.
28. In 1977 Keith was charged with possession of heroin in this city.
29. They played an outdoor concert here in August 1976.
30. Name the Rolling Stone TV special filmed in 1968 which was never aired.

21. David Bowie's wife.
22. Getting old
23. Hells Angels
24. *Black and Blue*
25. The Cockroaches
26. The New Barbarians
27. The Faces
28. Toronto, Canada
29. Knebworth, England
30. "Rock and Roll Circus"

BIG BANDS

Freshman Level

1. Who was Satchmo?
2. One of his big hits was "In The Mood."
3. Name the Miller song that had the phone number of a New York Hotel as its title.
4. This bandleader asked, "Is Everybody Happy?"
5. What was Lawrence Welk's theme song?
6. Baseball fans had Dizzy Dean but Big Band fans had Dizzy——.
7. Who was the Duke?
8. Who was the Count?
9. What was the Count's theme song?

10. This crooner was noted for singing through a megaphone.

1. Louis Armstrong
2. Glenn Miller
3. "Pennsylvania 6-5000"
4. Ted Lewis
5. "Bubbles in the Wine"
6. Gillespie
7. Duke Ellington
8. Count Basie
9. "One O'Clock Jump" or "April in Paris"
10. Rudy Vallee

Graduate Level

11. His theme song was "Racing with the Moon."
12. He was known as the Velvet Fog.
13. Who made "Minnie the Moocher" famous?
14. This trio made "The Boogie Woogie Bugle Boy" famous.
15. Who was the King of Swing?
16. Who was the King of Jazz?
17. Whose theme song was "I'm Getting Sentimental Over You"?
18. Name the U.S. dance-band leader who was known as the Waltz King?
19. Betty Grable married this band leader.
20. This U.S. child prodigy on drums played in vaudeville at age four.

11. Vaughan Monroe
12. Mel Tormé
13. Cab Calloway
14. The Andrew Sisters
15. Benny Goodman
16. Paul Whiteman
17. Tommy Dorsey
18. Wayne King
19. Harry James
20. Buddy Rich

Ph.D. Level

21. Name two famous trumpeters who died young and had the initials *B.B.*?
22. Name Bunny Berigan's theme song.
23. This bandleader had a close association with Jack Benny.
24. Singer Abbe Lane married this band leader.
25. This bandleader's son Ricky became a rock star.
26. Whose band featured a trio called the Rhythm Boys?
27. Name the Freddy Martin theme that was based on Tchaikovsky's Piano Concerto.
28. Who led the Pennsylvanians?
29. Whose theme song was "Artistry in Rhythm"?
30. Which bandleader was known as King?

21. Bunny Berigan and Bix Beiderbecke
22. "I Can't Get Started"
23. Phil Harris
24. Xavier Cugat
25. Ozzie Nelson
26. Paul Whiteman
27. "Tonight We Love"
28. Fred Waring
29. Stan Kenton
30. Joseph "King" Oliver

MUSIC: MUSICALS AND OPERETTAS

Provide the last word to complete the title.

Freshman Level

1. *Kiss Me* . . .
2. *Irma* . . .
3. *Naughty* . . .
4. *No, No* . . .
5. *Paint Your* . . .
6. *The Student* . . .
7. *The Wizard of* . . .
8. *Hello* . . .
9. *Funny* . . .
10. *My Fair* . . .

1. *Kate*
2. *La Douce*
3. *Marietta*
4. *Nanette*
5. *Wagon*
6. *Prince*
7. *Oz*
8. *Dolly*
9. *Girl*
10. *Lady*

Graduate Level

11. *Anything* . . .
12. *Girl* . . .
13. *The Merry* . . .
14. *Finian's* . . .
15. *Calamity* . . .
16. *Can* . . .
17. *Li'l* . . .
18. *Man of* . . .
19. *Hit the* . .
20. *Song of* . .

11. *Goes*
12. *Crazy*
13. *Widow*
14. *Rainbow*
15. *Jane*
16. *Can*
17. *Abner*
18. *La Mancha*
19. *Deck*
20. *Norway*

Ph.D. Level

21. *High* . . .
22. *Bye, Bye* . . .
23. *Bloomer* . . .
24. *South* . . .
25. *The Red* . . .
26. *Sweet* . . .
27. *On the* . . .
28. *Silk* . . .
29. *New* . . .
30. *Chorus* . . .

21. *Spirits*
22. *Birdie*
23. *Girl*
24. *Pacific*
25. *Mill*
26. *Charity*
27. *Town*
28. *Stockings*
29. *Moon*
30. *Line*

TRAGIC DEATHS

Freshman Level

1. Killed at age 24 in his Porsche, in California in 1955.
2. Died at 42 in 1977. Massive drug doses contributed to his death.
3. Murdered at age 37, in a parking lot in Los Angeles in 1977.
4. She died in 1962, reportedly from an overdose of sleeping pills.
5. She was decapitated when her car hit the back of a truck.
6. This producer died in the crash of his plane, *Lucky Liz*.
7. This male sex symbol and alcoholic died at age 50 in 1957.
8. This singer died of a drug overdose at age 47 in 1969.
9. This matinee idol died after an operation in 1926. He was 31.
10. This musician and composer was shot at age 40 in 1980.

1. James Dean
2. Elvis Presley
3. Sal Mineo
4. Marilyn Monroe
5. Jayne Mansfield
6. Michael Todd
7. Errol Flynn
8. Judy Garland
9. Rudolph Valentino
10. John Lennon

Graduate Level

11. She died of a brain tumor in 1975 at age 56.
12. She starred in *Born Yesterday* and died of cancer at age 42.
13. He died at age 43, in 1961, of blood poisoning following spinal surgery.
14. This singer succumbed to open heart surgery at age 37.
15. This war hero died at age 47 when his private plane crashed.
16. This rock star died in 1959 when his chartered plane crashed.
17. In 1964 this 51-year-old actor fell victim to alcohol and sedative poisoning, two years after attempting suicide.
18. This controversial comic died of an overdose in 1966.
19. This female 27-year-old rock singer died of a heroin overdose.
20. This star of the TV show *Chico and the Man* took his own life at the peak of his career.

11. Susan Hayward
12. Judy Holliday
13. Jeff Chandler
14. Bobby Darin
15. Audie Murphy
16. Buddy Holly
17. Alan Ladd
18. Lenny Bruce
19. Janis Joplin
20. Freddie Prinze

Ph.D. Level

21. After her death at age 36 it was revealed she had been secretly married to black musician Isaac Jones.
22. She starred in *A Streetcar Named Desire* and died of tuberculosis at age 53 in 1967.
23. She starred in *Genevieve* and died of leukemia in 1959 at 32.
24. He died at age 42 after falling down a flight of stairs.
25. This female jazz singer died at 39 from an overdose of pills.
26. This western singer died at 29 on New Year's Eve in 1953.
27. This actress died at age 43 in 1965 when a fire roared through her Chicago apartment.
28. This drummer of Led Zeppelin died in 1980 at age 32.
29. She married Vic Damone in 1954 but committed suicide at age 39 in 1971.
30. This actor appeared in *Rebel Without a Cause* with Sal Mineo and James Dean. He overdosed at age 37 in 1968.

21. Inger Stevens
22. Vivian Leigh
23. Kay Kendall
24. Jeffrey Hunter
25. Dinah Washington
26. Hank Williams
27. Linda Darnell
28. John Bonham
29. Pier Angeli
30. Nick Adams

COLE PORTER

Freshman Level: Complete the song title.

1. "You'd Be So Nice to———"
2. "What Is This Thing———"
3. "I Get a Kick———"
4. "In the Still———"
5. "I've Got You———"
6. "My Heart Belongs———"
7. "From This———"
8. "Get Out———"
9. "It's All Right———"
10. "I Concentrate———"

1. Come Home To.
2. Called Love?
3. out of You
4. of the Night
5. Under My Skin
6. to Daddy
7. Moment On
8. of Town
9. with Me
10. on You

Graduate Level: Provide the next three words of the lyrics.

11. "I Love Paris in the winter———"
12. "The eyes, the arms, the ———"
13. "For you and I have a guardian angel on high, with ———"
14. "People say in Boston even———"
15. "In the roaring traffic's boom, In the silence of———"
16. "Flying too high with some guy in the sky, Is my idea of———"
17. "You're the Nile, You're the———"
18. "It was just one of those nights, Just one of———"
19. "It brings back the sound of music so tender, it brings back a night———"
20. "But each time I do, just the thought of you makes me stop, ———"

11. when it drizzles
12. mouth of you
13. nothing to do
14. beans do it
15. my lonely room
16. nothing to do
17. Tow'r of Pisa
18. those fabulous flights
19. of tropical splendor
20. Before I begin

Ph. D. Level: Name the song that contains the given lyrics.

21. "Like the beat, beat, beat of the tom-tom."
22. "Birds do it, Bees do it."
23. "Who's prepared to pay the price, For a trip to paradise?"
24. "You're a melody, From a symphony by Strauss."
25. "If we'd thought a bit of the end of it, When we started painting the town."
26. "And here we are, planning to love forever, and promising never to part."
27. "So swell to keep ev'ry home-fire burning for."
28. "The skies are clear, And if you want to go walking, dear."
29. "Life's great, life's grand."
30. "If you're ever in a jam, Here I am."

21. "Night and Day"
22. "Let's Do It"
23. "Love for Sale"
24. "You're the Top"
25. "Just One of Those Things"
26. "Begin the Beguine"
27. "Easy To Love"
28. "It's De-Lovely"
29. "Ridin' High"
30. "Friendship"

COMEDIANS

Name the comedian from the given clue.

Freshman Level

1. He starred in *The Jerk*.
2. This silent-film star appeared in *City Lights* (1931).
3. He sang songs such as "Ink-a-Dink-a-Doo."
4. His radio show featured a hall closet full of junk.
5. A stand-up comic known for extremely insulting humour.
6. This comic gained fame as J.J. on *Good Times*.
7. This comedian "gets no respect."
8. He was born John Elroy Sanford.
9. His partner was Oliver Hardy.
10. He's best known as Barney Fife on *The Andy Griffith Show*.

1. Steve Martin
2. Charlie Chaplin
3. Jimmy Durante
4. Fibber McGee
5. Don Rickles
6. Jimmy Walker
7. Rodney Dangerfield
8. Redd Foxx
9. Stan Laurel
10. Don Knotts

Graduate Level

11. He is known for entertaining servicemen overseas.
12. He was Dean Martin's comic sidekick.
13. He was a regular on *Hollywood Squares* from 1966 to 1979.
14. This Canadian comedian is a noted impressionist.
15. She is noted for her fright-wigged, gravel-voiced routines.
16. He was the first black star in a TV series.
17. He was noted for his hard drinking and aversion to children and pets.
18. He was the top star of *Your Show of Shows*.
19. This piano player is noted for his one-man TV specials.
20. This ventriloquist's dummy was Charlie McCarthy.

11. Bob Hope
12. Jerry Lewis
13. Paul Lynde
14. Rich Little
15. Phyllis Diller
16. Bill Cosby
17. W. C. Fields
18. Sid Caesar
19. Victor Borge
20. Edgar Bergen

Ph.D. Level

21. He starred in the film *Animal House*.
22. His career was ruined by a scandal after the death of a starlet at a party he gave.
23. His films include *Bananas* and *Annie Hall*.
24. This star of the '30s was known for his wide mouth.
25. This meek-appearing actor was known as Mr. Peepers.
26. He created and starred in *Welcome Back Kotter*.
27. This sad-faced comic was a regular on *The Smothers Brothers*.
28. He played the Cowardly Lion in *The Wizard of Oz*.
29. This former schoolteacher wrote the best-seller *Sex and the Single Child*.
30. He was the first major star of TV's golden age, with a weekly program for Muriel Cigars.

21. John Belushi
22. Fatty Arbuckle
23. Woody Allen
24. Joe E. Brown
25. Wally Cox
26. Gabe Kaplan
27. Pat Paulsen
28. Bert Lahr
29. Sam Levenson
30. Ernie Kovacs

RADIO SHOWS

Freshman Level

1. She starred in *My Friend Irma*.
2. What was Irma's last name?
3. This was Rudy Valee's theme song.
4. He gave the blow-by-blow action in *Boxing from Madison Square Garden*.
5. Who sponsored the boxing program on radio?
6. What kind of car did Jack Benny own?
7. What was Jack's theme song?
8. He was the king of the cowboys in 1944.
9. This group sang with Roy for the first four years.
10. This was Roy's horse.

1. Marie Wilson
2. Peterson
3. "My Time Is Your Time"
4. Don Dunphy
5. Gillette
6. 1929 Maxwell
7. "Love in Bloom"
8. Roy Rogers
9. The Sons of the Pioneers
10. Trigger

Graduate Level

11. She played Baby Snooks for 14 years.
12. He was CBS's top news broadcaster in London during World War II.
13. This newscaster always ended with, "So long . . . until tomorrow."
14. Virginia Payne created this role.
15. Who was the dimwit dummy on the Edgar Bergen show?
16. Who was the man-chasing female dummy?
17. This wild-eyed comic with a big moustache was on Bob Hope's Pepsodent show.
18. Name the show's theme song.
19. What was the magic ingredient in Pepsodent?
20. What was the Great Gildersleeve's full name?

11. Fanny Brice
12. Edward R. Murrow
13. Lowell Thomas
14. Ma Perkins
15. Mortimer Snerd
16. Effie Klinker
17. Jerry Colonna
18. "Thanks for the Memory"
19. Irium
20. Throckmorton P.

Ph.D. Level

21. He played the marshall, Matt Dillon, on *Gunsmoke*.
22. He played Dagwood from 1939 to 1950.
23. Who played Blondie for most of the run?
24. Who was the best-known Sam Spade?
25. How did Spade end each program?
26. He was the emcee in 1935 on the *Shell Chateau* variety program.
27. Name Al Jolson's piano-playing sidekick from 1947 to 1949.
28. Name Kingfish's wife.
29. He played for Dr. James Kildare during the '40s.
30. Both Vincent Price and Barry Sullivan played this high-society crime fighter.

21. William Conrad
22. Arthur Lake
23. Penny Singleton
24. Howard Duff
25. "Period. End of report."
26. Al Jolson
27. Oscar Levant
28. Sapphire
29. Lew Ayres
30. The Saint

THEMES

NUMBERS

All of the answers are numbers.

Freshman Level

1. How many sides does a snowflake have?
2. How many blackbirds were baked in the pie?
3. How many legs does an insect have?
4. How many years did Rip Van Winkle sleep?
5. How many is a baker's dozen?
6. How many strings does a violin have?
7. How many people were at the Last Supper?
8. Jack Benny always gave this as his age.
9. How many pieces of silver did Judas receive?
10. How many voyages did Sinbad the Sailor make?

1. Six
2. Twenty-four
3. Six
4. Twenty
5. Thirteen
6. Four
7. Thirteen
8. Thirty-nine
9. Thirty
10. Seven

Graduate Level

11. How many nights in a fortnight?
12. How many handles does a goblet have?
13. How many squares are on a chessboard?
14. How many eggs did Luke eat in *Cool Hand Luke*?
15. What number on Pennsylvania Avenue is the White House?
16. According to Jaques in *As You Like It*, how many are the ages of man?
17. How many white stripes are on the U.S. flag?
18. How many flavors does Baskin-Robbins advertise?
19. What is the minimum age for a U.S. President?
20. What is the rent for a hotel on Boardwalk in Monopoly?

11. Fourteen
12. Zero
13. Sixty-four
14. Fifty
15. 1600
16. Seven
17. Six
18. Thirty-one
19. Thirty-five
20. Two thousand dollars

Ph.D. Level

21. What number was Patrick McGoohan on TV's *The Prisoner*?
22. How old was J. F. Kennedy when he was killed?
23. How many players are on a lacrosse team?
24. How many pounds was John Henry's hammer?
25. In pocket pool what number is the solid orange ball?
26. How many books are there in the New Testament?
27. What is the number of years mentioned in the opening of the Gettysburg Address?
28. How many bones are there in the human body?
29. How many letters are there in the Greek alphabet?
30. How many people saw Casey strike out?

21. Six
22. Forty-six
23. Twelve
24. Nine
25. Five
26. Twenty-seven
27. Eighty-seven
28. 206
29. Twenty-four
30. Five thousand

ANIMALS
All-of the answers are the names of animals.

Freshman Level

1.	He says, "Here I Come to Save the Day."	1.	Mighty Mouse
2.	Orphan Annie's dog.	2.	Sandy
3.	The Lone Ranger's horse.	3.	Silver
4.	This animal was made famous by Beatrix Potter.	4.	Peter Rabbit
5.	This tiger advertises Kellogg's Sugar Frosted Flakes.	5.	Tony the tiger
6.	This talking mule was featured in a number of films.	6.	Francis
7.	Roy Rogers' horse.	7.	Trigger
8.	The Flintstones' pet dinosaur.	8.	Dino
9.	A toy bear made famous by A. A. Milne.	9.	Winnie the Pooh
10.	Two cartoon chipmunks in Walt Disney movies.	10.	Chip 'n' Dale

Graduate Level

11.	Broom Hilda's pet buzzard.	11.	Gaylord
12.	Dr.Seuss's egg-hatching elephant.	10.	Horton
13.	Hopalong Cassidy's white horse.	13.	Topper
14.	The family dog on *My Three Sons*.	14.	Tramp
15.	Napoleon Bonaparte's horse.	15.	Marengo
16.	Alexander the Great's horse.	16.	Bucephalus
17.	This chimpanzee costarred with Ronald Reagan in a 1951 film.	17.	Bonzo
18.	The goldfish in the movie *Pinocchio*.	18.	Cleo
19.	This collie starred in many movies.	19.	Lassie
20.	The first dog to orbit the earth.	20.	Laika

Ph.D. Level

21.	The Phantom's gray wolf.	21.	Devil
22.	Dudley Do-Right's steed.	22.	Horse
23.	Zorro's black horse or his white horse.	23.	Tornado (black) Phantom (white)
24.	Tom Mix's horse.	24.	Tony
25.	The riderless horse at J. F. Kennedy's funeral.	25.	Blackjack
26.	Adolf Hitler's dog.	26.	Blondi
27.	Curly's horse in the 1955 movie *Oklahoma*	27.	Blue
28.	Cisco Kid's horse.	28.	Diablo
29.	The family dog of Hi and Lois Flagston.	29.	Dawg
30.	Ulysses S. Grant's horse.	30.	Cincinnatus

WOMEN
Each question and/or answer is connected to the theme "Women."

Freshman Level

1. The first female prime minister of England.
2. She played Edith Bunker.
3. Tony Orlando's two female singing companions were called.
4. She played Gloria Stivic.
5. She played the wicked witch in the Wizard of Oz.
6. She wrote *Little Women*.
7. This was Margaret Mitchell's only novel.
8. She wrote *Valley of the Dolls*.
9. She was the star of *The French Chef* TV cooking show.
10. The long time chief designer for Paramount Pictures.

1. Margaret Thatcher
2. Jean Stapleton
3. Dawn
4. Sally Struthers
5. Margaret Hamilton
6. Louisa May Alcott
7. *Gone with the Wind*
8. Jacqueline Susann
9. Julia Child
10. Edith Head

Graduate Level

11. Legend says she made the first American flag.
12. Leslie Hornby, top model of the late 1960's, was better known as . . .
13. She played Constance MacKenzie on TV's *Peyton Place*.
14. What did Jane Seymour, Catherine Howard, and Catherine Parr have in common?
15. She played the Good Witch, Glinda, in the Wizard of Oz.
16. Who were Anastasia and Drizella?
17. Canadian-born Gladys Smith was better known as . . .
18. She wrote *Fear of Flying*.
19. This novel written by D. H. Lawrence has the word *Women* in the title.
20. Alec Guiness and Peter Sellers play crooks involved with a seemingly harmless old lady in this 1955 film.

11. Betsy Ross
12. Twiggy
13. Dorothy Malone
14. Wives of Henry VIII
15. Billie Burke
16. Cinderella's stepsisters (Disney version)
17. Mary Pickford
18. Erica Jong
19. *Women in Love*
20. *The Lady Killers*

Ph.D. Level

21. Junko Tabei was the first woman to . . .
22. Her book *Etiquette* is the "Bible" of manners.
23. Her death in 1974 prompted Congress to hold hearings on health and safety problems in nuclear plants.
24. This popular Indian folk singer and songwriter supported the bid to return Alcatraz Island to native Americans.
25. This Black militant Communist International hero was the subject of the 1970 "Free Angela" movement.
26. This leader of Northern Ireland's civil rights movement became the youngest member of the British House of Commons.
27. This protest singer was a strong opponent of the War in Vietnam.
28. Which country had the first woman prime minister?
29. Hattie Wyatt Caraway was the first woman . . .
30. Mary Walker was the first U.S. female . . .

21. Scale Mount Everest
22. Emily Post
23. Karen Silkwood
24. Buffy Sainte-Marie
25. Angela Davis
26. Bernadette Devlin
27. Joan Baez
28. Ceylon (now Sri Lanka)
29. Elected to the U.S. Senate
30. Physician

MONEY
All answers relate to money.

Freshman Level

1. This term denotes money that must be accepted for debts.
2. The Bible says this is the root of all evil.
3. The unfinished object on the back of the U.S. single.
4. The largest bill now circulated in the U.S.
5. What metal was removed from U.S. coins after 1965?
6. The American Express Card says this word distinguishes it from all others.
7. To start Monopoly each player receives this amount.
8. What is the rent on Boardwalk with one hotel?
9. If you said the secret word on *You Bet Your Life* you won ——.
10. Dr. Joyce Brothers won the top prize in the category of boxing on this show.

1. Legal tender
2. "the love of money"
3. Pyramid
4. $100
5. Silver
6. Member
7. $1,500.
8. $2,000.
9. $100
10. *The $64,000 Question*

Graduate Level

11. In the film *Cabaret* Sally Bowles sings this song.

12. This 1966 film made Clint Eastwood an international star.
13. What was the 1967 sequel called?

14. What is the price tag on Minnie Pearl's hat?
15. Arthur Hailey's best-seller about the banking industry.
16. The secretary for James Bond's boss is named ——.
17. The first film directed by Woody Allen (1969).

18. Karen Black, Sandy Dennis, and Cher star in this 1982 film.

19. Title of a 1959 movie about Red Nichols.
20. Total price paid for the Louisiana Purchase.

11. "Money, Money, Money"
12. *A Fistful of Dollars*
13. *For a Few Dollars More*
14. $1.98
15. *The Money Changers*
16. Miss Moneypenny
17. *Take the Money and Run*
18. *Come Back to the Five and Dime, Jimmy Dean, Jimmy Dean*
19. *Five Pennies*
20. $15 million.

Ph. D. Level

21. Shelley Long and Tom Hanks star in this film.
22. On this Canadian island there is a famous money pit.

23. The Bay City Roller's had this No. 9 hit song in 1976.
24. What does the C stand for in J. C. Penney?
25. The only film in which Edward G. Robinson costarred with James Cagney (1931).
26. This term refers to the cash in public hands and checking accounts in the U.S.A.
27. On many credit cards this word appears if you erase the signature panel.
28. Although nearly invisible the name of twenty-six U.S. States appear on this bill.
29. Name the three presidents whose portraits appear not only on the U.S. coins but also bills and savings bonds ——.
30. The portraits of only two nonpresidents have been featured on U.S. coins in circulation. Name them.

21. *The Money Pit*
22. Oak Island, Nova Scotia
23. "Money Money"
24. Cash
25. *Smart Money*
26. M1
27. Void
28. $5 bill
29. Washington, Jefferson, Lincoln
30. B. Franklin, Susan B. Anthony

GROUPS OF PEOPLE

Identify the family, act, singing group, etc., from the given members.

Freshman Level

1. Chico, Harpo, Groucho, Zeppo.
2. John, George, Ringo, Paul.
3. Bashful, Grumpy, Dopey, Sleepy, Sneezy, Happy, Doc.
4. Huey, Dewey, Louie.
5. Adam, Eric (Hoss), Joe.

6. Ricky and David.
7. Matthew, Mark, Luke, John.
8. Athos, Porthos, Aramis.
9. Larry, Curly, Moe.
10. Butcher, Baker, Candlestick Maker.

1. Marx Brothers
2. Beatles
3. Seven Dwarfs
4. Donald Duck's nephews
5. Cartwright sons on *Bonanza*
6. Ozzie and Harriet's sons
7. Writers of the Gospels
8. Three Musketeers
9. Three Stooges
10. Three Men in a Tub

Graduate Level

11. Patty, Maxene, Laverne.
12. Cecile, Annette, Emilie, Marie, Yvonne.
13. Marcia, Jan, Cindy, Greg, Peter, Bobby.
14. Barry, Robin, Maurice.
15. Ditto, Dot, Chips, Trixie.

16. Mark, Bret, Bill.
17. Christine, Dorothy, Phillis.
18. Gaspar, Melchior, Balthasar.
19. Chang and Eng.
20. Karen and Richard.

11. Andrews Sisters
12. Dionne Quintuplets
13. Brady Bunch children
14. Bee Gees
15. Hi and Lois Flagston's children
16. Hudson Brothers
17. McGuire Sisters
18. Three Wise Men
19. Original Siamese twins
20. Carpenters

Ph.D. Level

21. Al, Jimmy, and Harry Joachim
22. Davey Jones, Peter Tork, Miky Dolenz, Mike Nesmith
23. Bernardo, Chris, Britt, Chico, Vin, Lee, and Harry.
24. Oren, Nash, Jason.
25. Alan, Wayne, Merrill, Jay, Donny, Marie, Jimmy.
26. Brynie, Charlie, Dick, Eddy, Mary, Madeleine, Irving.
27. Ed, Gene, Joe, Vic, Urick.
28. Mary Wilson, Florence Ballard, and Diana Ross.
29. John, Herbert, Harry, Donald.
30. Peter Yarrow, Paul Stookey, and Mary Travers.

21. Ritz Brothers
22. Monkees
23. Magnificent Seven
24. Over-the-Hill Gang
25. Osmonds
26. Seven Little Foys
27. Ames Brothers
28. Supremes
29. Mills Brothers
30. Peter, Paul, and Mary

MONTHS
All answers contain the name of a month.

Freshman Level

1.	This rabbit attended the Mad Hatter's tea party.	1.	March Hare
2.	This is Independence Day in the United States.	2.	July 4
3.	This month was named after Julius Caesar.	3.	July
4.	This month's name comes from the Latin word for seven.	4.	September
5.	This month is noted for "bustin' out all over."	5.	June
6.	Finish this line- "I shall love you in December with the love I gave in . . .	6.	May
7.	This month was named after the Roman god of beginnings.	7.	January
8.	Which month has neither an A nor an E in it?	8.	July
9.	These bring May flowers.	9.	April showers
10.	This date only occurs every fourth year.	10.	February 29

Graduate Level

11.	This musical features the songs "Sweetheart" and "Will You Remember?"	11.	*Maytime*
12.	This 1956 movie is based on a play about army officers involved with the Americanization of post WW-II Okinawa.	12.	*The Teahouse of the August Moon*
13.	This month was named after the Roman god of war.	13.	March (Mars)
14.	This month was named after the first Roman Emperor.	14.	August (Augustus)
15.	Finish this line, "Oh, it's a long, long while from . . .	15.	May to December
16.	Finish this line, "But the days grow short, when you reach . . .	16.	September
17.	This is Guy Fawkes Day.	17.	November 5
18.	These four months have thirty days.	18.	November, April, June, and September
19.	If your sign is Virgo, you were born in one of two months.	19.	August, September
20.	This is the name of a large American department store chain.	20.	May Company

Ph.D. Level

21.	Doris Day and Ray Bolger have shipboard problems in this 1952 musical movie.	21.	*April in Paris*
22.	Pat Boone falls in love with Shirley Jones in this 1957 musical movie.	22.	*April Love*
23.	This 1948 Movie stars Bette Davis and Robert Montgomery as magazine writers.	23.	*June Bride*
24.	In this 1947 British film, John Mills tries to prove he's innocent of homicide.	24.	*The October Man*
25.	Finish this line: "And what is so rare as . . .	25.	a day in June?
26.	This is the only month which has two Rs in it.	26.	February
27.	This book by Josephine Winslow Johnson won a Pulitzer Prize in 1935.	27.	*Now in November*
28.	If your sign is Pisces, you were born in one of these two months . . .	28.	February, March
29.	Burt Reynolds played this detective on TV.	29.	Dan August
30.	This was the girl from UNCLE in the TV series starring Stefanie Powers	30.	April Dancer

WORDS, WORDS, WORDS

QUOTATIONS
Name the person identified with the quotation.

Freshman Level

1. I want to be alone.
2. The only thing we have to fear is fear itself.
3. I shall return.
4. I have nothing to offer but blood, toil, tears, and sweat.
5. How to win friends and influence people.
6. Come up and see me sometime.
7. You ain't heard nothin' yet, folks.
8. I think that I shall never see a poem lovely as a tree.
9. But I have promises to keep, and miles to go before I sleep.
10. The Sudetenland is the last territorial claim I have in Europe.

1. Greta Garbo
2. Franklin D. Roosevelt
3. Douglas MacArthur
4. Winston Churchill
5. Dale Carnegie
6. Mae West
7. Al Jolson
8. Joyce Kilmer
9. Robert Frost
10. Adolf Hitler

Graduate Level

11. It ain't a fit night out for man or beast.
12. Mr. Watson, come here, I want you.
13. From each according to his abilities, to each according to his needs.
14. How do I love thee? Let me count the ways.
15. I believe it is peace for our time.
16. Speak softly and carry a big stick.
17. I have been to the mountain.
18. England expects every man will do his duty.
19. He who can does, he who cannot teaches.
20. Mad dogs and Englishmen go out in the midday sun.

11. W. C. Fields
12. Alexander Graham Bell
13. Karl Marx
14. Elizabeth Barrett Browning
15. Neville Chamberlain
16. Theodore Roosevelt
17. Martin Luther King, Jr.
18. Horatio Nelson
19. George Bernard Shaw
20. Noel Coward

Ph.D. Level

21. Let there be spaces in your togetherness.
22. I never met a man I didn't like.
23. That's all there is; there isn't any more.
24. The fog comes on little cat feet.
25. The bullet that will kill me is not yet cast.
26. Give me liberty, or give me death.
27. Little strokes fell great oaks.
28. I think, therefore I am.
29. The devil can cite Scripture for his purpose.
30. These I have loved: White plates and cups, clean gleaming, The cool kindness of sheets . . .

21. Kahlil Gibran
22. Will Rogers
23. Ethel Barrymore
24. Carl Sandburg
25. Napoleon Bonaparte
26. Patrick Henry
27. Benjamin Franklin
28. René Descartes
29. William Shakespeare
30. Rupert Brook

NAMES OF THINGS

Give the name of the thing from the information provided.

Freshman Level

1. The fingers of a fork
2. Wide neck scarf that is tied under the chin
3. Flat round hat with a tight headband
4. Frame to support space rockets prior to lift-off
5. Middle or body of a church
6. Back of the neck
7. Stocking-like hat without a brim
8. Support for an artist's canvas
9. Overstuffed footstool
10. Instrument used in geometry to measure angles

1. Tines
2. Ascot
3. Beret
4. Gantry
5. Nave
6. Nape
7. Toque
8. Easel
9. Ottoman
10. Protractor

Graduate Level

11. Bundle of sticks
12. Mixture of spirits and water
13. Projecting rim to keep a wheel on the track
14. Hair clip
15. Scottish woolen cap with a wide crown and a pompom.
16. Grotesque carved figures projecting from roofs of churches
17. Sailing vessel between a corvette and a destroyer in size
18. Receptacle for holy water
19. Small pocket just below the front waistband of trousers
20. Wooden device with holes for the head and hands, used for publicly punishing offenders

11. Fagot
12. Grog
13. Flange
14. Barrette
15. Tam-o-shanter
16. Gargoyles
17. Frigate
18. Font
19. Fob
20. Pillory

Ph.D. Level

21. Covering on the tip of a shoelace
22. Small shallow dish with cover, used for cultures
23. Cloth band worn around the arm
24. Small metal hoop that supports a lampshade
25. Indentation at the bottom of some wine bottles
26. Belt that encircles the waist and passes over the shoulder
27. Large iron grating to prevent passage through a gateway
28. Wicker basket (often in pairs) suspended over the back of a beast of burden
29. A broad triangular part above a portico or door
30. Tuft (as of feathers) on a helmet

21. Aglet
22. Petri dish
23. Brassard
24. Harp
25. Kick or punt
26. Sam Browne belt
27. Portcullis
28. Pannier(s)
29. Pediment
30. Panache

WORDS WITH TRIPLE MEANINGS

Give one word that fits all three meanings. All answers are three-letter words.

Freshman Level

1. A piano part; a door opener; a Florida reef
2. A drinking vessel; the hole in golf; a trophy
3. Noah's son; a type of meat; a poor actor
4. An unopened flower; fellow; to produce
5. To flow rapidly; a baseball score; a tear in a stocking
6. An acting signal; a pigtail; a pool stick
7. A clothes fastener; a bowling target; a leg
8. A radio chain; a profit; a snare
9. A shallow incline; a swim; a pickpocket
10. Advance information; a gratuity; an extremity

1. Key
2. Cup
3. Ham
4. Bud
5. Run
6. Cue
7. Pin
8. Net
9. Dip
10. Tip

Graduate Level

11. A dance; an air trip; used to make beer
12. A jail; a quill; a sty
13. A level surface; the river bottom; a place to sleep
14. A harbor obstruction; a drinking spot; a lever
15. A baseball club; a winged animal, a spree
16. A line; a boat ride; a brawl
17. Fate; a movie studio; a great deal
18. A haircut; a pendulum weight; a shilling
19. A draw; a railway plank; a cravat
20. Prepared; to put; a group of articles

11. Hop
12. Pen
13. Bed
14. Bar
15. Bat
16. Row
17. Lot
18. Bob
19. Tie
20. Set

Ph.D. Level

21. A metal dish; a Greek god; a filming technique
22. Attitude; atmosphere; a song
23. A track; a fixed practice; sexual excitement
24. A small drink; cheese tang, a pinch
25. A joke; to choke; a device to keep the jaws open
26. Part of a bridle; a small piece; one's contribution
27. A maxim; a cutting tool; observed
28. To judge; to attempt; to play in rugby
29. Charge; a burden; to enter in a list
30. A metal; to place in cans; people in northeast Thailand

21. Pan
22. Air
23. Rut
24. Nip
25. Gag
26. Bit
27. Saw
28. Try
29. Tax
30. Tin

COLORFUL WORDS

All of the answers contain a color. For example, to the clue "She was attacked by a wolf," the answer is "Red Riding Hood."

Freshman Level

1.	Relief organization	1.	Red Cross
2.	The foam on a wave	2.	Whitecap
3.	Bubonic Plague	3.	Black Death
4.	Architects' plans	4.	Blueprints
5.	Well-born person	5.	Blueblood
6.	Air raid precaution	6.	Blackout
7.	Train porter	7.	Red cap
8.	Seller of vegetables	8.	Green grocer
9.	British soldier of the past	9.	Red coat
10.	Children's story about a horse	10.	*Black Beauty*

Graduate Level

11.	Novice	11.	Greenhorn
12.	Golf course charge	12.	Greens fee
13.	Illegal sale of goods	13.	Black market
14.	Mercury	14.	Quicksilver
15.	The day of the market collapse	15.	Black Friday
16.	Policeman	16.	Bluecoat
17.	Fib or small untruth	17.	White lie
18.	Murderer who killed his wives	18.	Bluebeard
19.	Plaza in Moscow	19.	Red Square
20.	First prize	20.	Blue ribbon

Ph.D. Level

21.	1920s dance	21.	Black bottom
22.	Motion pictures	22.	Silver screen
23.	New York's Bohemia	23.	Greenwich Village
24.	To make something or someone appear good	24.	Whitewash
25.	Scenic spot in Capri	25.	Blue Grotto
26.	Edit	26.	Blue pencil
27.	Italian Fascist group under Mussolini	27.	Blackshirts
28.	Troublesome possession	28.	White elephant
29.	A pirate in *Treasure Island*	29.	Long John Silver
30.	The name of the schooner on the Canadian dime	30.	*Bluenose*

WORD COMBINATIONS
What word could be placed in front of each of the three given words to make a new term?

Freshman Level

1. Out, mail, sheep
2. Deck, dial, beam
3. Market, man, natural
4. Pick, ache, less
5. Able, cloth, room
6. Proof, tight, wheel
7. Skin, tape, cap
8. Some, bill, made
9. Turn, lap, flow
10. Bone, ground, bite

1. Black
2. Sun
3. Super
4. Tooth
5. Wash
6. Water
7. Red
8. Hand
9. Over
10. Back

Graduate Level

11. Bid, cast, rage
12. Start, roar, right
13. Stream, hill, pour
14. Back, breed, past
15. Piece, key, mind
16. Head, off, spring
17. Fast, through, neck
18. Bread, cut, coming
19. Port, hop, fare
20. Slip, boy, lick

11. Out
12. Up
13. Down
14. Half
15. Master
16. Well
17. Break
18. Short
19. Car
20. Cow

Ph.D. Level

21. Time, weed, picker
22. Land, form, vest
23. Hood, hole, date
24. Road, bar, bones
25. Go, study, take
26. Gap, over, watch
27. Fruit, shot, vine
28. Horn, bow, hand
29. Attack, part, point
30. Due, contract, let

21. Rag
22. In
23. Man
24. Cross
25. Under
26. Stop
27. Grape
28. Long
29. Counter
30. Sub

PARTS OF THINGS
Name the thing that contains all three given parts.

Freshman Level

1.	Arc, radius, sector	1.	Circle
2.	Pulp, crown, root	2.	Tooth
3.	Liner, tread, belts	3.	Tire
4.	Fork, frame, sprocket	4.	Bicycle
5.	Skirt, pommel, stirrup	5.	Saddle
6.	Corolla, filament, stigma	6.	Flower
7.	Pupil, iris, cornea	7.	Eye
8.	Concave lens, eyepiece, focusing screw	8.	Telescope
9.	Percussion, cellos, bassoons	9.	Orchestra
10.	Headstall, cheek straps, curb bit	10.	Bridle

Graduate Level

11.	Tarsus, metatarsus, phalanges	11.	Human foot
12.	Subject, verb, object	12.	Sentence
13.	Nuclear membrane, cytoplasm, nucleus	13.	Cell
14.	Butt, jowl, ham	14.	Pig
15.	tie beam, struts, rafters	15.	Roof
16.	Epidermal cells, palisade cells, veins	16.	Leaf
17.	Shroud lines, risers, harness	17.	Parachute
18.	Shoe, drum, lining	18.	Brake
19.	Root, prefix, suffix	19.	Word
20.	Hammer, anvil, stirrup	20.	Ear

Ph.D. Level

21.	Mandible, lateral line, dorsal fin	21.	Fish
22.	Tye, yoke, bowline	22.	Sail (square)
23.	Throat, foxing, platform	23.	Shoe
24.	Back flat, teaser, wings	24.	Stage
25.	Garboard, bar keel, beam	25.	Hull
26.	Saddle, wattles, spur	26.	Cock
27.	Maxillary palpus, abdomen, metathorax	27.	Insect
28.	Girdle, table, corner facet	28.	Diamond
29.	Bridge, chin rest, fingerboard	29.	Violin
30.	Epiglottis, trachea, pharynx	30.	Throat

SPORTS

TERMINOLOGY, NUMBER ONE
Name the sport identified with each term.

Freshman Level

1. Tee
2. Bird
3. TKO
4. Let
5. Eagle
6. Balk
7. Par
8. Love
9. Slalom
10. Power Play

1. Golf
2. Badminton
3. Boxing
4. Tennis
5. Golf
6. Baseball
7. Golf
8. Tennis
9. Skiing
10. Hockey

Graduate Level

11. Blitz
12. Bogey
13. ERA
14. Skip
15. Service break
16. Audible
17. Bonspiel
18. Clipping
19. Hat trick
20. One-two

11. Football
12. Golf
13. Baseball
14. Curling
15. Tennis
16. Football
17. Curling
18. Football
19. Hockey
20. Boxing

Ph.D. Level

21. Pivot
22. Schuss
23. Traveling
24. Match play
25. Moguls
26. Salchow
27. Anchor
28. Spike
29. Caber
30. Axel

21. Basketball
22. Skiing
23. Basketball
24. Golf
25. Golf
26. Figure skating
27. Relay Racing
28. Volleyball, football
29. Scotch games
30. Figure skating

TERMINOLOGY, NUMBER TWO

Name the sport identified with each term.

Freshman Level

1. Turnover
2. Épée
3. Gutter
4. Stumps
5. Keyhole
6. Carom
7. House
8. Duster
9. Dunk
10. Scratch

1. Football, basketball
2. Fencing
3. Bowling
4. Cricket
5. Basketball
6. Billiards, pool
7. Curling
8. Baseball
9. Basketball
10. Pool, Horseracing

Graduate Level

11. Knocked up
12. Zamboni
13. Clothesline
14. Tote board
15. Gainer
16. Jerk
17. English
18. Foil
19. Free kick
20. Keystone base

11. Badminton
12. Hockey
13. Football
14. Horseracing
15. Diving
16. Weightlifting
17. Pool
18. Fencing
19. Soccer
20. Baseball

Ph.D. Level

21. Stonewalling
22. Telltale
23. Bridge
24. Chic chac
25. Crawl
26. Free fall
27. Egg position
28. Hands
29. Pigeon
30. Scrum

21. Cricket
22. Squash
23. Pool
24. Jai alai
25. Swimming
26. Sky diving
27. Skiing
28. Soccer
29. Shooting
30. Rugby

ATHLETES
Name the sport with which each athlete is associated.

Freshman Level

1. Jack Johnson
2. Jacques Plante
3. Willie Shoemaker
4. Ty Cobb
5. Jean-Claude Killy
6. Herschel Walker
7. John Weissmuller
8. Rocky Marciano
9. Tom Kite
10. Bryan Trottier

1. Boxing
2. Hockey
3. Horse racing
4. Baseball
5. Skiing
6. Football
7. Swimming
8. Boxing
9. Golfing
10. Hockey

Graduate Level

11. Pancho Gonzales
12. Dazzy Vance
13. Ken Anderson
14. Paavo Nurmi
15. Don Schollander
16. Frank Shorter
17. Dixie Walker
18. Jack Kramer
19. Pele
20. Althea Gibson

11. Tennis
12. Baseball
13. Football
14. Distance runner
15. Swimming
16. Distance runner
17. Baseball
18. Tennis
19. Soccer
20. Tennis

Ph.D. Level

21. Wally Moon
22. Zack Wheat
23. Emil Zatopek
24. Walter Hagen
25. Don Budge
26. Gertrude Ederle
27. Grover Cleveland Alexander
28. Henry Armstrong
29. Sammy Baugh
30. Eddie Arcaro

21. Baseball
22. Baseball
23. Running
24. Golf
25. Tennis
26. Swimming
27. Baseball
28. Boxing
29. Football
30. Horse Racing

BASEBALL

Freshman Level

1. First position in the batting order
2. Number four position in the batting order
3. Illegal pitch deliberately thrown at a batter's head
4. Affectionate term for a manager
5. Ball deliberately pitched at least a foot wide of the plate so that the batter cannot hit it
6. Play in which the ball is thrown with the intention of catching a base runner off base and tagging him out
7. Section of cheaper seats exposed to the elements
8. Area adjoining the baseball field where relief pitchers warm up
9. Relief pitcher who specializes in entering the game when the opposing team is threatening to score
10. Area between the individual outfielders

1. Leadoff
2. Cleanup
3. Beanball
4. Skipper
5. Pitchout
6. Pickoff
7. Bleachers
8. Bullpen
9. Fireman
10. Gap

Graduate Level

11. Team's best pitcher, usually a starter
12. Pitcher and catcher as a unit is known as the . . .
13. Pitcher's mound
14. Play in which the runner breaks for second base and the batter is obliged to hit the ball to protect the runner
15. Symbol that designates a strikeout when keeping a scorecard
16. Second game of a double-header
17. In position to be the next hitter
18. Running catch by an outfielder, made close to his shoe tops
19. Second base
20. Double play in which the third baseman throws to the second baseman, who then throws to the first baseman

11. Ace
12. Battery
13. Hill
14. Hit-and-run
15. K
16. Nightcap
17. On deck
18. Shoestring catch
19. Keystone
20. Around the horn

Ph.D. Level

21. Term for a batting style in which the hitter moves his front foot sideways, away from the plate as he swings at the ball
22. Long, thin bat used to hit flies and grounders during practice
23. Improperly thrown curve that fails to break sharply or curves lazily on a flat plane
24. Feat where a batter hits a single, double, triple, and home run in one game
25. Area deep in the infield and far to the right of the shortstop
26. Base runner's lead, how far he positions himself off base, and the quickness of his start in a stolen base attempt
27. Pitcher's assortment of softly thrown pitches that includes only breaking balls, off-speed deliveries, or knuckleballs
28. Traditional pregame ritual in which a player standing at close range throws to another player who bats the ball crisply to players in front of him
29. Amount of contact between the bat and the pitch
30. Fly ball within easy reach of an outfielder

21. Foot in the bucket
22. Fungo
23. Hanging curve
24. Hit for the cycle
25. In the hole
26. Jump
27. Junk
28. Pepper
29. Wood
30. Can of corn

GOLF

Freshman Level

1. Warning to let golfers know that they are in danger of being hit by a golf ball
2. Closely cropped grass that lies between the tee and the green
3. Score an expert player would be expected to make on a given hole
4. Ball hit with a right-to-left curve
5. Take one's stance and adjust the club preparatory to hitting the ball
6. Score one less than par on a hole
7. Obstacle such as a sand trap or grassy depression constituting a hazard
8. Closely cut grassy area that surrounds the hole
9. Allowance of strokes intended to even competition between two golfers of unequal ability
10. Edge of the cup

1. Fore
2. Fairway
3. Par
4. Hook
5. Address the ball
6. Birdie
7. Bunker
8. Green
9. Handicap
10. Lip

Graduate Level

11. Cluster of spectators around the green in a tournament
12. Any golf course obstacle
13. Flagstick
14. Specially designed close-cropped area from which the first shot on a hole is taken
15. Score of one over par on a hole
16. Score of two strokes under par on a hole
17. Mishit a shot and cause it to dribble along the ground
18. Expression meaning to hit the ball above the middle
19. OB stands for . . .
20. Areas, usually of long grass, off the fairway

11. Gallery
12. Hazard
13. Pin
14. Tee
15. Bogey
16. Eagle
17. Dub (flub)
18. Top the ball (hit it on the head)
19. Out-of-bounds
20. Rough

Ph.D. Level

21. After the tee shots, this term is used to designate the golfer farthest from the hole, who plays first.
22. Right to drive first from the next tee
23. Coat awarded to the winner of the Masters Tournament
24. Large billboard type of display showing the current standing in relation to par of the leaders of a medal tournament
25. Traffic directors for the gallery
26. Free second shot off the first tee, if the first shot is bad
27. Putted ball that hits the cup, goes around the back of it, rolling on the edge, and shoots back out toward the golfer
28. Rain water in a fairway or rough
29. Illegal "stealing" an inch closer to the hole in replacing a ball marked on the green
30. Ball lying directly in the path of another player's ball on the line to the cup

21. Away
22. Honor
23. Green jacket
24. Leader board
25. Marshals
26. Mulligan
27. Buttonhook
28. Casual water
29. Hunching
30. Stymie

TROPHIES

Provide the name of the trophy awarded.

Freshman Level

1. Outstanding college football player in the U.S.A.
2. The amateur athlete of the year in the U.S.A.
3. The winner of the NHL play-offs.
4. The leading goalie in the NHL.
5. The world team tennis competition for women.
6. The world team tennis competition for men.
7. For international 12-meter yacht racing.
8. The MVP award in the NHL.
9. The best pitcher in the major leagues.
10. The best overall contribution to team and baseball.

1. Heisman Trophy
2. James E. Sullivan Award
3. Stanley Cup
4. Vezina Trophy
5. Federation Cup
6. Davis Cup
7. America's Cup
8. Hart Trophy
9. Cy Young Award
10. Roberto Clemente Award

Graduate Level

11. Team tennis between Great Britain and the U.S.A.
12. The best defenseman in the NHL.
13. The most sportsmanlike player in the NHL.
14. The best rookie in the NHL.
15. The most valuable player in the NBA.
16. The nation's outstanding interior lineman in college football.
17. The nation's best lineman in college football.
18. The best collegiate football team of the season (voted on by football writers)
19. The winner of the Super Bowl.
20. Most outstanding relief pitcher in the major leagues.

11. Wightman Cup
12. James Norris Trophy
13. Lady Byng Trophy
14. Calder Trophy
15. Podoloff Trophy
16. Outland Award
17. Lombardi Award
18. Grantland Rice Trophy
19. Vince Lombardi Trophy
20. Relief Man Award

Ph.D. Level

21. The best defensive forward in the NHL.
22. The most valuable player in the NHL playoffs.
23. The most valuable NFL player.
24. The award for most tournament victories in women's golf.
25. The award for most tournament victories in men's golf.
26. For consistency as shown by low-strokes-per-round during tournament play.
27. This was the cup awarded to the winner of the now defunct World Hockey Association.
28. For sustained contributions to the development of sport.
29. The Canadian football champions.
30. For international soccer.

21. Frank J. Selke Trophy
22. Conn Smythe Trophy
23. Jim Thorpe Trophy
24. Mickey Wright Award
25. Bryon Nelson Award
26. Vardon Trophy
27. Avco World Trophy
28. Henry Stone Award
29. Grey Cup
30. World Cup

MISCELLANEOUS

Freshman Level

1. This team won the 1983 Super Bowl.
2. This team lost in the 1983 Super Bowl game.
3. He quarterbacked the 1983 Super Bowl champions.
4. This team won the 1982 World Series.
5. This team lost in the 1982 World Series.
6. This team won the 1982–1983 Stanley Cup.
7. This team lost in the 1982–83 Stanley Cup Series.
8. Where were the Winter Olympics held in 1980?
9. Which team won the Olympic gold for hockey in 1980?
10. He won five gold medals for speed skating in the '80 Olympics.

1. Washington Redskins
2. Miami Dolphins
3. Joe Theismann
4. St. Louis Cardinals
5. Milwaukee Brewers
6. New York Islanders
7. Edmonton Oilers
8. Lake Placid, N.Y.
9. U.S.A.
10. Eric Heiden

Graduate Level

11. This hockey team set a pro record for unbeaten games with a thirty-five game streak.
12. This team holds the North American record for all professional sports of thirty-three consecutive wins.
13. Who won the men's singles at Wimbledon in 1982?
14. This New York Yankee was killed in a plane crash in 1979.
15. Who was the American goalie in the 1980 Winter Olympics?
16. Which team won the 1982 NBA playoff championship?
17. Which team lost in the 1982 NBA finals?
18. Who won the 1982 U.S. Tennis Open for men?
19. Who won the 1982 U.S. Open in golf?
20. Who won the 1982 U.S. Tennis Open for women?

11. Philadelphia Flyers
12. Los Angeles Lakers
13. Jimmy Connors
14. Thurman Munson
15. Jim Craig
16. Los Angeles Lakers
17. Philadelphia 76ers
18. Jimmy Connors
19. Tom Watson
20. Chris Evert

Ph.D. Level

21. Hanns Wenzel won this country's first ever Olympic gold medal, in the 1980 Winter Olympics.
22. Name the Russian goalie who was replaced in the Olympics of 1980 by Mychkin.
23. Who won the women's singles at Wimbledon in 1982?
24. Who formed the NHL Players' Association?
25. This team has won the Canadian football championship five years in a row. Its fifth win was in 1982.
26. This horse won the Kentucky Derby in 1983.
27. This horse won the Preakness in 1982.
28. This U.S. yacht won the 1980 America's Cup.
29. This team won the NASL (soccer) championship game (1982).
30. This country won the World Cup of soccer in 1982.

21. Liechtenstein
22. Tretiak
23. Martina Navratilova
24. Alan Eagleson
25. Edmonton Eskimos
26. Sunny's Halo
27. Conquistador Cielo
28. *Freedom*
29. New York Cosmos
30. Italy

THE IMPOSSIBLE SPORTS QUIZ
Only real sports buffs should attempt this difficult quiz.

Freshman Level

1. Which horse was first to win the Triple Crown?
2. Holds the track record for winning the Kentucky Derby.
3. Holds the record for most home runs (23) with the bases filled.
4. This Buffalo Bill quarterback had only one interception on 151 attempts during the 1976 season.
5. Which quarterback established a record in 1964 with seventeen consecutive passes completed?
6. Who wrote the book *The Education of a Tennis Player*?
7. Which basketball team set an NBA record with twenty consecutive losses in 1973?
8. Who was the second heavyweight boxing champion of the world?
9. This quarterback led the NFL in passing a total of six times.
10. How many seasons did Hank Aaron hit fifty or more homers?

1. Sir Barton (1919)
2. Secretariat (1973)
3. Lou Gehrig
4. Joe Ferguson
5. Bert Jones
6. Rod Laver
7. Philadephia 76ers
8. James J. Corbett
9. Sammy Baugh
10. Never

Graduate Level

11. Name the only two men who have won baseball's Triple Crown more than once.
12. Which team, in 1964 had a seven-game lead with only two weeks left in the season but lost the National League pennant?
13. Greg Meyer won the 87th running of this race.
14. In 1977 this Canadian nineteen-year-old became the first woman to complete a double crossing of the English Channel.
15. The longest recorded holed putt in a major tournament was eighty-six feet in the 1955 Masters Tournament. Who shot it.?
16. Which golfer won a record nineteen golf tournaments in 1945?
17. Who was the only player to score four straight game-winning goals in Stanley Cup play?
18. Which NBA basketball player played in 1270 games.
19. This Philadelphia Warrior basketball player led the NBA in scoring for three consecutive years, 1953 to 1955.
20. He won the 1983 Indy 500.

11. Ted Williams, Rogers Hornby
12. Philadelphia Phillies
13. The Boston Marathon
14. Cynthia Nicholas
15. Cary Middlecoff
16. Byron Nelson
17. Clark Gillies
18. John Havlicek
19. Neil Johnston
20. Tom Sneva

Ph.D. Level

21. The first Wimbledon championship was held in . . .
22. Who was first to score three-hundred career goals in the NHL?
23. Name the three players on the Chicago Black Hawks 1946–1947 Pony Line.
24. Which goalie won the MVP trophy in 1954 but was named to neither the first nor second NHL All-Star team?
25. Which player holds the NBA record for most personal fouls?
26. In 1901 this baseball player had a batting average of .422.
27. Who was the first black baseball player in the American League?
28. Who was the youngest major league baseball player (15 years)?
29. He won the U.S. singles tennis championship seven times.
30. In 1976 he threw the discus three times and set three world records.

21. 1877
22. Nels Steward (1938)
23. Max and Doug Bentley and Bill Mosienko
24. Al Rollins
25. Hal Greer
26. Napoleon Lajoie
27. Larry Doby
28. Joe Nuxhall
29. Bill Tilden
30. Mac Wilkens

SCIENCE

SCIENTIFIC AND TECHNICAL TERMS

Freshman Level

1. A particle carrying a negative charge
2. The most important ore of aluminum
3. Molten material under the earth's surface
4. A unit of electrical resistance named after a man
5. Inflammation of the colon
6. Molten material that issues from a volcano
7. An instrument for measuring an electric current
8. Any product of human workmanship
9. An instrument for measuring distance above the ground
10. Sensitivity to certain substances

1. Electron
2. Bauxite
3. Magma
4. Ohm
5. Colitis
6. Lava
7. Ammeter
8. Artifact
9. Altimeter
10. Allergy

Graduate Level

11. A scale of wind velocity from 0 to 12
12. The application of mathematics to biology
13. Any triangular structure
14. An apparatus to separate two liquids by high speed rotation
15. This law states that at any given temperature the volume of gas varies inversely as the pressure.
16. The study of projectiles in motion
17. What is a Btu?
18. What is EMF?
19. A conical mass hanging from the roof of caverns
20. A method for dating ancient objects, using carbon

11. Beaufort scale
12. Biometrics
13. Deltoid
14. Centrifuge
15. Boyle's Law
16. Ballistics
17. British thermal unit
18. Electro-motive force
19. Stalactite
20. Radiocarbon dating

Ph.D. Level

21. Rock formed from a molten state
22. The pressure of 1,000 Dynes per square cm.
23. Genetic variation in living things which appears suddenly
24. Irregular in form; not divisible into halves
25. A map line connecting places of equal atmospheric pressure
26. A unit on a chromosome
27. Region where a nerve impulse moves from axone to dendrite
28. The splitting of an atomic nucleus
29. A collodial suspension of one liquid in another
30. Regions in latitudes 30'N and S with high atmospheric pressure and light winds.

21. Igneous rock
22. Millibar
23. Mutation
24. Asymmetric
25. Isobar
26. Gene
27. Synapse
28. Fission
29. Emulsion
30. Horse Latitudes

GENERAL

Freshman Level

1. What does a botanist study?
2. Some animals spend the winter in a sleeplike state known as . . .
3. The planet closest to the sun is . . .
4. An animal is a fish if it has . . .
5. How many more legs do spiders have than insects?
6. Animals that once existed but don't now are said to be . . .
7. What is the name for a branch of a river?
8. An animal is a bird if it has . . .
9. Which science studies weather?
10. The study of living things is known as . . .

1. Plants
2. Hibernation
3. Mercury
4. Gills
5. Two
6. Extinct
7. Tributary
8. Feathers
9. Meteorology
10. Biology

Graduate Level

11. This makes grass and leaves green.
12. Animals with bony skeletons are called . . .
13. A narrow strip of land joining two larger masses of land is known as an . . .
14. The study of man and culture is known as . . .
15. Snakes are reptiles. What are frogs?
16. This mineral is the hardest natural substance.
17. The Milky Way is a . . .
18. The study of animals is known as . . .
19. Map lines showing longitude are called . . .
20. By what chemical process do plants manufacture food?

11. Chlorophyll
12. Vertebrates
13. Isthmus
14. Anthropology
15. Amphibians
16. Diamond
17. Galaxy
18. Zoology
19. Meridians
20. Photosynthesis

Ph.D. Level

21. The three types of rocks are metamorphic, sedimentary, and . . .
22. What is the study of rocks and minerals called?
23. Any slippage along a fracture in the earth's surface is known as a . . .
24. This is the most malleable of all metals.
25. The three parts of an insect's body are; head, thorax, and . . .
26. Meat-eating animals are called . . .
27. The four stages in the life-cycle of an insect are: egg, adult, pupa, and . . .
28. What is the lightest known substance?
29. This term denotes "cone-bearing" trees.
30. Ichthyology is the study of . . .

21. Igneous
22. Geology
23. Fault
24. Gold
25. Abdomen
26. Carnivores
27. Larva
28. Hydrogen
29. Conifers
30. Fish

ANIMALS: GROUPS

Given the name of an animal, provide the word that is used for a group of those animals. For example, a group of cows is a herd.

Freshman Level

1.	Ants	1.	Colony
2.	Gorillas	2.	Band
3.	Hens	3.	Brood
4.	Lions	4.	Pride
5.	Partridges	5.	Covey
6.	Fish	6.	School
7.	Kangaroos	7.	Troop
8.	Geese	8.	Flock, gaggle
9.	Chicks	9.	Brood, clutch
10.	Oysters	10.	Bed

Graduate Level

11.	Larks	11.	Exaltation
12.	Bees	12.	Hive, swarm
13.	Cats	13.	Clowder, clutter
14.	Ducks	14.	Brace, team, flock
15.	Horses	15.	Pair, team, herd
16.	Hounds	16.	Pack
17.	Leopards	17.	Leap
18.	Parrots	18.	Company
19.	Pheasants	19.	Nest, nide, nye
20.	Sheep	20.	Drove, flock

Ph.D. Level

21.	Goats	21.	Trip
22.	Wolves	22.	Pack
23.	Whales	23.	Pod
24.	Storks	24.	Mustering
25.	Elks	25.	Gang
26.	Owls	26.	Parliament
27.	Rats	27.	Rabble
28.	Toads	28.	Knot
29.	Ponies	29.	String
30.	Hummingbirds	30.	Charm

MATHEMATICS

Freshman Level

1. What is 4 divided by 1/2?   1. 8
2. What is 1/4 divided by 1/4?   2. 1
3. What number is 3 less than half of 50?   3. 22
4. What is 32 ° Fahrenheit in Celsius?   4. 0°
5. If apples are 25¢ each, how much will half a dozen cost?   5. $1.50
6. What is the area of a room 12′ × 11′?   6. 132 square feet
7. What is the perimeter of a room 9′ × 11′?   7. 40 feet
8. How many nickles are there in $2.25?   8. 45
9. If a bill is $1.82 what is the change from $5.00?   9. $3.18
10. At 50 mph how long will it take to go 325 miles?   10. 6 1/2 hours

Graduate Level

11. Approximately how many inches are there in a meter?   11. 39
12. How much is 2% of 400?   12. 8
13. Express 2/5 as a decimal.   13. .4
14. How much is two squared plus three squared?   14. 13
15. If A + B = 63 and B is 18, what is A?   15. 45
16. A 720-cubic-foot room is 10′ × 9′. What is its height?   16. 8 feet
17. The scores were 16, 20, and 27. What was the average?   17. 21
18. How many quarts in 2 1/2 gallons?   18. 10
19. If the temperature is 15°F and drops 18 degrees, what is the temperature?   19. −3°F
20. If the temperature is 15°C and drops 18 degrees, what is the temperature?   20. −3°C

Ph.D. Level

21. What is the square root of 144?   21. 12
22. If a pen and pencil set cost $2.50 and the pen costs $1.00 more than the pencil, how much is the pencil?   22. 75¢
23. What is (16 + 5) × 2, divided by 7?   23. 6
24. If you travel 10,000 miles and use five new tires equally, how many miles will each tire experience?   24. 8,000 miles
25. If 6 men can dig 6 holes in 6 minutes, how long will it take 10 men to dig 10 holes?   25. 6 minutes
26. If two sides of a right-angled triangle are 3″ and 4″, how long is the hypotenuse?   26. 5 inches
27. How many months in 3 1/4 years?   27. 39
28. How many square meters in a square kilometer?   28. 1,000,000
29. If sweaters costing $20 are reduced 15% what's the price?   29. $17
30. What is 25 divided by .5?   30. 50

SPACE

Freshman Level

1. Name the largest planet in our solar system.
2. How many planets are there?
3. Who was the first person on the moon?
4. Name the comet that appears every 76.3 years.
5. What is the proper name for "falling stars"?
6. What is the name for a pattern formed by a group of stars?
7. What is the ocean of air around the earth called?
8. What name is given to immense systems of billions of stars?
9. What is the prevalent theory for the origin of the universe called?
10. How many times does the earth revolve around the sun per year?

1. Jupiter
2. Nine
3. Neil Armstrong
4. Halley's Comet
5. Meteors
6. Constellation
7. Atmosphere
8. Galaxies
9. Big Bang
10. Once

Graduate Level

11. What is the name for the "minor planets"?
12. What is the term for the path followed by a body in space?
13. Our galaxy is commonly called . . .
14. What is a light year?

15. What is the common name for the Aurora Borealis?
16. Name the smallest known planet in the solar system.
17. What is the science that studies space and the objects within it?
18. What is the abbreviated name for the American agency responsible for the space program?
19. Name the theoretical end-product of the gravitational collapse of a massive star.
20. What is the name for the upper atmosphere?

11. Asteroids
12. Orbit
13. The Milky Way
14. The distance light travels in one year
15. Northern Lights
16. Pluto
17. Astronomy
18. NASA
19. Black hole
20. Stratosphere

Ph.D. Level

21. What was the name for the first U.S. manned space program?
22. What was the name for America's first earth-orbiting space station?
23. Who made the first manned orbital flight?
24. The Big Dipper is part of what constellation?
25. What does the name mean in English?
26. What is the main component of air?
27. What are these: Ceres, Juno, Iris, and Flora?
28. The tilt of the earth's axis accounts for what?
29. What do these stars have in common: Sirius, Vega, Rigel, and Canopus?
30. The spiral galaxy nearest to ours is the . . .

21. Mercury
22. *Skylab*
23. Yuri Gagarin
24. Ursa Major
25. Big Bear
26. Nitrogen
27. Asteroids
28. Seasons
29. Extreme brightness
30. Andromeda

PHYSICS

Freshman Level

1. The ability to do work is called . . .
2. The space occupied by a body is called its . . .
3. The quantity of matter that a body contains is its . . .
4. The force that brings moving bodies to a halt is . . .
5. The tendency of moving bodies to continue their motion is called . . .
6. The standard unit of mass in the metric system is the . . .
7. Mass per unit volume is . . .
8. This instrument measures atmospheric pressure.
9. The pivot point of a lever is called the . . .
10. Name this law: If the temperature of a gas is kept constant its volume will vary inversely to its pressure.

1. Energy
2. Volume
3. Mass
4. Friction
5. Inertia
6. Gram
7. Density
8. Barometer
9. Fulcrum
10. Boyle's law

Graduate Level

11. Work equals force multiplied by . . .
12. The tendency of bodies in circular motion to fly off at a tangent is called . . .
13. One thousand watt-hours is a . . .
14. A device used to change the voltage of alternating currents is a . . .
15. Poor conductors are called . . .
16. The amount of moisture in the air is the . . .
17. This instrument measures relative humidity.
18. The two types of waves are transverse and . . .
19. If light can't pass through it, it is . . .
20. The rays of light that fall upon an object are called . . .

11. Distance
12. Centrifugal effect
13. Kilowatt-hour
14. Transformer
15. Insulators
16. Humidity
17. Hygrometer
18. Longitudinal
19. Opaque
20. Incident rays

Ph.D. Level

21. A point to which rays of light converge is called a . . .
22. The visible spectrum of light ranges from red to . . .
23. These waves are important for photography and tanning . . .
24. The center of an atom is called its . . .
25. Circuits can be wired in series or in . . .
26. The positive terminal is called the . . .
27. Watts = Volts × ?.
28. How do you convert from Fahrenheit to Celcius?
29. Change 41° Fahrenheit to Celcius.
30. Einstein's formula for energy is . . .

21. Focus
22. Violet
23. Ultraviolet
24. Nucleus
25. parallel
26. Anode
27. Amperes
28. $(F-32) \times 5/9 = C$
29. $5°C$
30. $E = mc^2$

MUSIC AND ART

SONGS ASSOCIATED WITH PEOPLE

Name the person most closely associated with the given song.

Freshman Level

1.	"When the Moon Comes Over the Mountain"	1.	Kate Smith
2.	"Thanks for the Memory"	2.	Bob Hope
3.	"I Did It My Way"	3.	Frank Sinatra
4.	"Making Whoopee"	4.	Eddie Cantor
5.	"Where the Blue of the Night Meets the Gold of the Day"	5.	Bing Crosby
6.	"Inka Dinka Doo"	6.	Jimmy Durante
7.	"Somewhere Over the Rainbow"	7.	Judy Garland
8.	"Racing with the Moon"	8.	Vaughn Monroe
9.	"As Time Goes By"	9.	Humphrey Bogart
10.	"Mule Train"	10.	Frankie Laine

Graduate Level

11.	"Donkey Serenade"	11.	Allen Jones
12.	"Lullaby of Birdland"	12.	George Shearing
13.	"The Twist"	13.	Chubby Checker
14.	"That Old Black Magic"	14.	Billy Daniels
15.	"Moonlight Serenade"	15.	Glenn Miller
16.	"Doggy in the Window"	16.	Patti Page
17.	"Be My Love"	17.	Mario Lanza
18.	"Oh My Papa"	18.	Eddie Fisher
19.	"Mammy"	19.	Al Jolson
20.	"La Vie en Rose"	20.	Edith Piaf

Ph.D. Level

21.	"The Bluebird of Happiness"	21.	Jan Peerce
22.	"The Wheel of Fortune"	22.	Kay Starr
23.	"Take the A Train"	23.	Duke Ellington
24.	"I'm a Yankee Doodle Dandy"	24.	George M. Cohan
25.	"My Man"	25.	Fanny Brice
26.	"Carolina Moon"	26.	Morton Downey
27.	"Love in Bloom"	27.	Jack Benny
28.	"I'm Just a Vagabond Lover"	28.	Rudy Vallee
29.	"Cara Mia Mine"	29.	David Whitfield
30.	"It's So Nice to Have This Hour Together"	30.	Carol Burnett

OSCAR-WINNING SONGS
Given the year and the movie, name the song that won the Oscar.

Freshman Level

1. 1976 *A Star Is Born*
2. 1975 *Nashville*
3. 1974 *The Towering Inferno*
4. 1972 *The Poseidon Adventure*
5. 1969 *Butch Cassidy and the Sundance Kid*
6. 1967 *Doctor Dolittle*
7. 1964 *Mary Poppins*
8. 1961 *Breakfast at Tiffany's*
9. 1959 *A Hole in the Head*
10. 1948 *The Paleface*

1. "Evergreen."
2. "I'm Easy"
3. "We May Never Love Like This Again"
4. "The Morning After"
5. "Raindrops Keep Falling on My Head"
6. "Talk to the Animals"
7. "Chim Chim Cher-ee"
8. "Moon River"
9. "High Hopes"
10. "Buttons and Bows"

Graduate Level

11. 1965 *The Sandpiper*
12. 1956 *The Man Who Knew Too Much*
13. 1947 *Song of the South*
14. 1945 *State Fair*
15. 1944 *Going My Way*
16. 1942 *Holiday Inn*
17. 1940 *Pinocchio*
18. 1939 *The Wizard of Oz*
19. 1937 *Waikiki Wedding*
20. 1935 *Gold Diggers of 1935*

11. "The Shadow of Your Smile"
12. "Que Sera, Sera"
13. "Zip-A-Dee-Doo-Dah"
14. "It Might As Well Be Spring"
15. "Swinging on a Star"
16. "White Christmas"
17. "When You Wish upon a Star"
18. "Over the Rainbow"
19. "Sweet Leilani"
20. "Lullaby of Broadway"

Ph.D. Level

21. 1978 *Thank God It's Friday*
22. 1957 *The Joker is Wild*
23. 1953 *Calamity Jane*
24. 1951 *Here Comes the Groom*
25. 1949 *Neptune's Daughter*
26. 1943 *Hello Frisco*
27. 1941 *Lady Be Good*
28. 1938 *Big Broadcast of 1938*
29. 1936 *Swing Time*
30. 1934 *The Gay Divorcee*

21. "Last Dance"
22. "All the Way"
23. "Secret Love"
24. "In the Cool, Cool, Cool of the Evening"
25. "Baby It's Cold Outside"
26. "You'll Never Know"
27. "The Last Time I Saw Paris"
28. "Thanks for the Memory"
29. "The Way You Look Tonight."
30. "The Continental"

BROADWAY MUSICALS
Given two song titles from the musical score, name the Broadway musical.

Freshman Level

1. "Hello Young Lovers"; "Shall We Dance?"
2. "Hey There"; "Hernando's Hideaway"
3. "You Are Love"; "Ol' Man River"
4. "Surrey with the Fringe on Top"; "Out of My Dreams"
5. "Some Enchanted Evening"; "Younger Than Springtime"
6. "Tradition"; "Matchmaker, Matchmaker"
7. "Let the Sun Shine In"; "Aquarius"
8. "The Quest"; "Dulcinea"
9. "If Ever I Would Leave You"; "What Do the Simple Folk Do?"
10. "Tonight"; "I Feel Pretty"

1. *The King and I*
2. *Pajama Game*
3. *Showboat*
4. *Oklahoma*
5. *South Pacific*
6. *Fiddler on the Roof*
7. *Hair*
8. *Man of La Mancha*
9. *Camelot*
10. *West Side Story*

Graduate Level

11. "There's No Business Like Showbusiness"; "They Say It's Wonderful"
12. "'S Wonderful"; "Let's Kiss and Make Up"
13. "There Is Nothing Like a Dame"; "Bali Ha'i"
14. "Seventy-Six Trombones"; "Till There Was You"
15. "Bewitched, Bothered, and Bewildered"; "I Could Write a Book"
16. "Tea for Two"; "I Want to be Happy"
17. "Tomorrow Belongs to Me"; "If You Could See Her"
18. "What I Did for Love"; "Hello Twelve, Hello Thirteen, Hello Love"
19. "I Enjoy Being a Girl"; "A Hundred Million Miracles"
20. "Tomorrow"; "Easy Street"

11. *Annie Get Your Gun*
12. *Funny Face*
13. *South Pacific*
14. *The Music Man*
15. *Pal Joey*
16. *No No Nanette*
17. *Cabaret*
18. *A Chorus Line*
19. *Flower Drum Song*
20. *Annie*

Ph.D. Level

21. "If I Were a Bell"; "A Bushel and a Peck"
22. "Whatever Lola Wants"; "Heart"
23. "Night and Day"; "I've Got You on My Mind"
24. "I've Got a Crush on You"; "Soon"
25. "Diamonds Are a Girl's Best Friend"; "A Little Girl from Little Rock"
26. "My Funny Valentine"; "The Lady Is a Tramp"
27. "Sometimes I'm Happy"; "Hallelujah"
28. "Dancing in the Dark"; "New Sun in the Sky"
29. "A Real Nice Clambake"; "June Is Bustin' Out All Over"
30. "C'est Magnifique"; "I Love Paris"

21. *Guys and Dolls*
22. *Damn Yankees*
23. *Gay Divorcee*
24. *Strike Up the Band*
25. *Gentlemen Prefer Blondes*
26. *Babes in Arms*
27. *Hit the Deck*
28. *Bandwagon*
29. *Carousel*
30. *Can-Can*

HOLLYWOOD MUSICALS

Given the date of the movie and two songs from the score, name the musical.

Freshman Level

1. 1964 "A Spoonful of Sugar"; "Feed the Birds"
2. 1946 "Swanee"; "April Showers"
3. 1964 "The Rain in Spain"; "I Could Have Danced All Night"
4. 1939 "If I Only Had a Brain"; "Ding, Dong, the Witch Is Dead"
5. 1965 "Climb Every Mountain"; "Maria"
6. 1951 "Make Believe"; "Life Upon the Wicked Stage"
7. 1935 "The Indian Love Call"; "The Song of the Mounties"
8. 1955 "I Cain't Say No"; "Kansas City"
9. 1956 "We Kiss in a Shadow"; "I Whistle a Happy Tune"
10. 1945 "It's a Grand Night for Singing"; "It Might as Well be Spring"

1. *Mary Poppins*
2. *The Jolson Story*
3. *My Fair Lady*
4. *The Wizard of Oz*
5. *The Sound of Music*
6. *Showboat*
7. *Rose Marie*
8. *Oklahoma*
9. *The King and I*
10. *State Fair*

Graduate Level

11. 1956 "If I Loved You"; "You'll Never Walk Alone"
12. 1955 "Luck Be a Lady"; "Sit Down You're Rocking the Boat"
13. 1953 "Too Darn Hot"; "So in Love"
14. 1935 "Tramp, Tramp, Tramp"; "I'm Falling in Love with Some-one"
15. 1950 "I Wanna be Loved by You"; "Who's Sorry Now?"
16. 1952 "Make 'Em Laugh"; "You Were Meant for Me"
17. 1954 "Drink, drink, drink"; Summertime in Heidelberg"
18. 1959 "I Got Plenty of Nothin' "; "It Ain't Necessarily So"
19. 1969 "I Talk to the Trees"; "They Call the Wind Maria"
20. 1958 "Thank Heaven for Little Girls"; "I Remember It Well"

11. *Carousel*
12. *Guys and Dolls*
13. *Kiss Me Kate*
14. *Naughty Marietta*
15. *Three Little Words*
16. *Singing in the Rain*
17. *The Student Prince*
18. *Porgy and Bess*
19. *Paint Your Wagon*
20. *Gigi*

Ph.D. Level

21. 1969 "Put on Your Sunday Clothes"; "So Long, Dearie"
22. 1954 "Auf Wiedershen"; "Lover Come Back to Me"
23. 1968 "Old Devil Moon"; "How Are Things in Glocca Morra?"
24. 1942 "I Remember You"; "Tangerine"
25. 1968 "You Are Woman, I am Man"; "Don't Rain on My Parade"
26. 1942 "Be Careful, It's My Heart"; "Happy Holiday"
27. 1935 "Cheek to Cheek"; "Isn't This a Lovely Day?"
28. 1950 "Crazy Rhythm"; "I Want to be Happy"
29. 1969 "What Did I Have That I Don't Have Now?"; "He Isn't You"
30. 1943 "But Not for Me"; "Embraceable You"

21. *Hello Dolly*
22. *Deep In My Heart*
23. *Finian's Rainbow*
24. *The Fleet's In*
25. *Funny Girl*
26. *Holiday Inn*
27. *Top Hat*
28. *Tea for Two*
29. *On a Clear Day You Can See Forever*
30. *Girl Crazy*

COMPOSERS

Name the composer of the given musical work.

Freshman Level

1. "Stardust"
2. "White Christmas"
3. *Showboat*
4. "If You Could Read My Mind"
5. "The Blue Danube"
6. "Swanee"
7. *Madame Butterfly*
8. "Don't Fence Me In"
9. "Ah, Sweet Mystery of Life"
10. "This Can't Be Love"

1. Hoagy Carmichael
2. Irving Berlin
3. Jerome Kern
4. Gordon Lightfoot
5. Johann Strauss
6. George Gershwin
7. Giacomo Puccini
8. Cole Porter
9. Victor Herbert
10. Richard Rogers

Graduate Level

11. "Liebestraum"
12. "Claire de Lune"
13. "Blue Tango"
14. *H.M.S. Pinafore*
15. "Moonlight Sonata"
16. *The Student Prince*
17. "Feelings"
18. "Let It Be"
19. "American Pie"
20. "When I Fall in Love"

11. Franz Liszt
12. Claude Debussy
13. Leroy Anderson
14. Sir Arthur Sullivan
15. Ludwig van Beethoven
16. Sigmund Romberg
17. Morris Albert
18. John Lennon and Paul McCartney
19. Don McLean
20. Victor Young

Ph.D. Level

21. "The Very Thought of You"
22. "I'm an Old Cowhand"
23. "Moon River"
24. "You've Got a Friend"
25. "Revolutionary Etude"
26. "If You Go Away"
27. "Sixteen Tons"
28. "Make It Easy On Yourself"
29. "Song of India"
30. "Maple Leaf Rag"

21. Ray Noble
22. Johnny Mercer
23. Henry Mancini
24. Carole King
25. Frederic Chopin
26. Jacques Brel
27. Merle Travis
28. Burt Bacharach
29. Nicolai Rimsky-Korsakov
30. Scott Joplin

POP AND ROCK

Freshman Level

1. She is Loretta Lynn's younger sister.
2. This singer owns a valuable collection of eyeglasses.
3. He had a hit in 1956 with "Just Walking in the Rain."
4. This is the greatest-selling soundtrack album ever.
5. Sid Vicious was a member of this punk rock group.
6. He is known as The Polish Prince.
7. Her first big hit was "Snowbird."
8. He made his movie debut as a singer in *The Godfather*.
9. She was the first female country singer to receive a platinum record.
10. For which song did she receive the platinum record?

1. Crystal Gayle
2. Elton John
3. Johnnie Ray
4. *Saturday Night Fever*
5. Sex Pistols
6. Bobby Vinton
7. Anne Murray
8. Al Martino
9. Dolly Parton
10. "Here You Come Again"

Graduate Level

11. This group is called Billy J. Kramer and the . . .
12. This group is called Country Joe and the . . .
13. This group is called Gary Puckett and the . . .
14. This group is called Kenny Rogers and the . . .
15. This Kiss member is noted for his long tongue.
16. This singer was a Rhodes scholar, wrote several books, and was a Golden Gloves boxer.
17. He was once employed as a page boy at CBS and wrote jingles for State Farm Insurance.
18. This member of the *Carol Burnett Show* had a bit hit in 1973 with "The Night the Lights Went Out in Georgia."
19. She recorded "The Morning After" for *The Poseidon Adventure* and "We May Never Love Like This Again" for *The Towering Inferno*. Both won Oscars.
20. This three-time Academy Award-winning actor had a hit called "Dutchman's Gold" and one called "Old Rivers."

11. Dakotas
12. Fish
13. Union Gap
14. First Edition
15. Gene Simmons
16. Kris Kristofferson
17. Barry Manilow
18. Vicki Lawrence
19. Maureen McGovern
20. Walter Brennan

Ph.D. Level

21. Carl Perkins's version of this 1956 hit was the first record to make the pop, country, and R&B charts at the same time.
22. Both Steve Lawrence (1962) and Donny Osmond (1971) had number-one hits with their versions of this song.
23. He made his TV debut on *American Bandstand* with his fly open.
24. This performer toured with both Elvis Presley and the Beatles when they were first beginning.
25. What do Clyde McPhatter, Ben E. King, and Bobby Hendricks have in common?
26. This Calypso singer was the first singer to win an Emmy.
27. Duane Allman and Berry Oakley, members of the Allman Brothers Band, were both killed. What was unusual about their deaths?
28. She sang the theme song of the 1966 movie *Alfie*.
29. He played Buddy Holly in *The Buddy Holly Story*.
30. He sang the theme song for the movie *In the Heat of the Night*.

21. "Blue Suede Shoes"
22. "Go Away Little Girl"
23. Tony Orlando
24. Roy Orbison
25. All were lead singers of The Drifters
26. Harry Belafonte
27. Both killed on motorcycles in Macon, Georgia (1971 & 1972)
28. Cher
29. Gary Busey
30. Ray Charles

ART: GENERAL, NUMBER ONE

Freshman Level

1. A frame that supports a painting in progress is called an . . .
2. The thin oval board on which an artist mixes his colours is called a . . .
3. An artistic arrangement of wires, etc., hung so as to be easily set in motion, is called a . . .
4. Painting, drawing, music, and dancing are known as the 'fine arts.' Printing, photography, and bookmaking are known as the . . .
5. Paintings made on plaster that is still moist are called . . .
6. What is the opposite of a "realistic" painting?

7. Cartoonist Alfred Gerald Caplin was better known as . . .
8. He is best known for his covers for the *Saturday Evening Post*.
9. This Dutch painter was noted for thick brushstrokes and brilliant colors.
10. He won an Emmy for *A Charlie Brown Christmas*.

1. Easel
2. Palette
3. Mobile
4. Graphic arts
5. Frescoes
6. Abstract or non-objective
7. Al Capp
8. Norman Rockwell
9. Vincent Van Gogh
10. Charles Schulz

Graduate Level

11. He is best known for his "Believe It Or Not" cartoons.
12. Folk painter Anna Mary Robertson is better known as . . .
13. *Arrangement in Gray and Black, No. 1*, is better known as . . .
14. A sculpture of three Confederate figures appears on the face of this mountain in Georgia.
15. This surrealist painter is noted for combining realistic details into unreal, dream fantasy pictures.
16. *Card Players* was painted by . . .
17. In which city is the world's largest art gallery?
18. Beautiful writing, usually with brush and ink, is called . . .
19. This early American cabinetmaker worked in New York.
20. Various natural earths used as yellow, brown, or red pigments are known as . . .

11. Robert Ripley
12. Grandma Moses
13. *Whistler's Mother*
14. Stone Mountain
15. Salvador Dali
16. Paul Cezanne
17. Leningrad
18. Calligraphy
19. Duncan Phyfe
20. Ocher

Ph.D. Level

21. He drew the famous *Birds of America*.
22. This English illustrator is best known for his decadent, sensual, black-and-white drawings.
23. He led the "Pop" art movement and is noted for his paintings of such items as soup cans.
24. *The Milkmaid* and *The Man with the Hoe* were by . . .
25. This Greek painter was noted for his unorthodox, elongated treatment of devotional subjects.
26. He sculpted *St. George and the Dragon*.
27. He designed the Washington Monument.
28. This American cartoonist's first name is Jules.
29. This Greek sculpted *The Temple of Theseus*.
30. This French artist painted some of his finest pictures in Tahiti.

21. John James Audubon
22. Aubrey Beardsley
23. Andy Warhol
24. Jean-Francois Millet
25. El Greco
26. Donatello
27. Robert Mills
28. Jules Feiffer
29. Phidias
30. Paul Gauguin

ART: GENERAL, NUMBER TWO

Freshman Level

1. *The Blue Boy* was painted by . . .
2. *The Archer* was sculpted by . . .
3. *The Kiss* was sculpted by . . .
4. The architect of St. Paul's Cathedral in London was . . .
5. A composition made by pasting various materials or objects to form a work of art is called . . .
6. The *Mona Lisa* was painted by . . .
7. *David* was sculpted by . . .
8. *Starry Night* was painted by . . .
9. *Whistler's Mother* was painted by . . .
10. The architect of the Guggenheim Museum was . . .

1. Thomas Gainsborough
2. Henry Moore
3. Auguste Rodin
4. Christopher Wren
5. Collage
6. Leonardo da Vinci
7. Michelangelo
8. Vincent van Gogh
9. James Whistler
10. Frank Lloyd Wright

Graduate Level

11. *Three Musicians* was painted by . . .
12. *At the Moulin Rouge* was painted by . . .
13. The architect of St. Peter's Cathedral in Rome was . . .
14. A wall painting is called a . . .
15. The pieta was a common theme. What is it?

16. The famous *Last Supper* fresco in Milan was painted by . . .
17. A composition made by fitting together pictures or parts of pictures is called a . . .
18. A large oven in which pottery is fired is called a . . .
19. A painting of inanimate objects is called a . . .
20. A design formed by embedding objects such as small pieces of stone or glass in cement is called a . . .

11. Pablo Picasso
12. Toulouse-Lautrec
13. Michelangelo
14. Mural
15. The Virgin grieving over the dead Christ
16. Leonardo da Vinci
17. Montage
18. Kiln
19. Still life
20. Mosaic

Ph.D. Level

21. *Young Woman with a Water Jug* was painted by . . .
22. The ceiling of the Sistine Chapel was painted by . . .
23. *Raising of the Cross* was painted by . . .
24. A saltcellar for a king was sculpted by . . .
25. The famous art museum in Paris is the . . .
26. The movement that stressed absurdity and that challenged established artistic and literary conventions was called . . .
27. *The Shrimp Girl* was painted by . . .
28. He is acknowledged as the greatest master of the Dutch school.
29. A hard-baked clay used for sculpture and as a building material is called . . .
30. He invented pointillism.

21. Jan Vermeer
22. Michelangelo
23. Peter-Paul Rubens
24. Benvenuto Cellini
25. Louvre
26. Dada
27. William Hogarth
28. Rembrandt
29. Terra-cotta
30. Georges Seurat

MISCELLANY

Freshman Level

1. Monks live in monasteries. Where do nuns live?
2. Frank Sinatra, Sammy Davis, Dean Martin, and Peter Lawford were reportedly members of this group.
3. He hosted *American Bandstand.*
4. Eddy Haskell and Clarence "Lumpy" Rutherford were characters in this TV series.
5. What was Beaver's family name?
6. Which nationality cannot join the French Foreign Legion?
7. He had the lead in *Hogan's Heroes.*
8. What was the name of the Six Million Dollar Man in the TV series?
9. Name the four "colored" seas.

10. Name two of the Confederate States that don't end in A.

1. In convents
2. The Clan (Rat Pack)

3. Dick Clark
4. *Leave It to Beaver*

5. Cleaver
6. French
7. Bob Crane
8. Col. Steve Austin

9. Black, Red, White, Yellow
10. Mississippi, Texas, Tennessee, Arkansas

Graduate Level

11. This is the favorite food of both detective Columbo and Robert Ironside.
12. Charles Foster Kane was the publisher of this newspaper.
13. How many years is a millenium?
14. He was the commandant of Stalag 13 on *Hogan's Heroes.*
15. He is the police commissioner of Gotham on TV's *Batman.*
16. The hop, skip, and jump event is now known as the . . .
17. He played private eye Cannon on TV.
18. Maxwell Smart worked for this agency in *Get Smart.*
19. Name the rival evil agency.
20. Cousin Itt was a hairy character on this TV show.

11. Chili

12. *Inquirer*
13. Thousand
14. Commandant Klink
15. Commissioner Gordon
16. Triple jump
17. William Conrad
18. CONTROL
19. KAOS
20. *The Addams Family*

Ph.D. Level

21. Charlie Chicken was a friend of this comic book character.
22. A unit of information used in computers is called a . . .
23. Chi Chi is in London Zoo. It's a . . .
24. Chucky Margolis was a character in a comedy routine by this group.
25. This turtle lived with Pogo in the Okefenokee Swamp.
26. This was the pseudonym of World War II spy Elyesa Bazna.
27. Who played Elyesa Bazna in the 1952 movie?
28. What was the movie called?
29. What did Presidents James Garfield, Harry Truman, and Gerald Ford have in common?
30. This was the country east of Eden where Cain lived after killing Abel.

21. Andy Panda
22. Bit
23. Giant panda
24. Hudson Brothers

25. Churchy La Femme
26. Cicero
27. James Mason
28. *Five Fingers*
29. Left-handed

30. Land of Nod

Freshman Level

1. What are the four dimensions?
2. What is the minimum number of victories to become an air ace?
3. In the Bible, how many days and nights did it rain?
4. You use this to play Russian roulette.
5. What is a single-humped camel called?
6. This fictional bull was noted for smelling flowers.
7. On which radio show did Throckmorton P. Gildersleeve appear?

8. He was the Barber of Seville.
9. This is the most southerly state of the U.S.A.
10. This company produces the bodies for General Motors.

1. Length, width, depth, time
2. Five
3. Forty
4. Revolver
5. Dromedary
6. Ferdinand
7. *Fibber McGee and Molly*

8. Figaro
9. Hawaii
10. Fisher

Graduate Level

11. This is the most westerly state of the U.S..
12. The value of a diamond is determined by the four C's. What are they?
13. This was the only part of Britain captured by Germany in World War II.
14. The Four Horsemen of the Apocalypse represent Conquest, Pestilence, and what else?
15. How many lines are there in a sonnet?
16. This mineral helps our bones to grow strong.
17. How long does a fifteen-round boxing match take from start to finish?
18. This actor and humorist's real name was William Claude Dukinfield.
19. In the movie *Pinocchio* what was the name of Gepetto's cat?
20. The First Brooklyn Savings Bank was robbed in this 1976 movie starring Al Pacino.

11. Alaska
12. Color, cut, carat, clarity
13. Channel Islands

14. Famine, Death

15. Fourteen
16. Calcium
17. Fifty-nine minutes

18. W.C. Fields

19. Figaro
20. *Dog Day Afternoon*

Ph.D. Level

21. What does Charlie Brown's father do for a living?
22. Singer Gerry Dorsey goes by the name of the composer of the opera *Hansel and Gretel*. He is known as . . .
23. He played Ensign Pulver in the 1955 movie *Mister Roberts*.
24. His epitaph is "Free at last, free at last, thank God Almighty I'm free at last."
25. What did Allan Williams, Brian Epstein, and Alan Klein have in common?
26. Movie character Eric Claudin was better known as . . .
27. Lily Tomlin created this telephone operator role.
28. Celeste Geyer, circus fat lady, was known as . . .
29. This was once the home ballpark of the Brooklyn Dodgers.
30. He said, "I'm gonna kill dat cwazy wabbot."

21. Barber
22. Englebert Humperdinck

23. Jack Lemmon
24. Martin Luther King

25. Managers of the Beatles

26. Phantom of the Opera
27. Ernestine
28. Dolly Dimples
29. Ebbets Field
30. Elmer Fudd

Freshman Level

1.	He was the religious member of Robin Hood's band.	1. Friar Tuck
2.	He was known as the friendly snowman.	2. Frostie
3.	Which sport did the Gashouse Gang play?	3. Baseball
4.	This 650-pound bear had a TV series.	4. *Gentle Ben*
5.	Flip Wilson portrayed this female character.	5. Geraldine Jones
6.	He was Hitler's architect.	6. Albert Speer
7.	How many ghosts appeared to Ebenezer Scrooge?	7. Four
8.	Which ghost was the first to appear?	8. Marley's ghost
9.	How many events are in the pentathlon?	9. Five
10.	The flight recorder on airplanes is called the "black box." What color is it really?	10. Orange

Graduate Level

11.	Ron Galella was a New York photographer noted for hounding this celebrity.	11. Jacqueline Kennedy
12.	This was Baretta's pet, white, twenty year-old cockatoo.	12. Fred
13.	When would a ship hoist the Blue Peter?	13. Before leaving harbor
14.	This was the nickname of Frances Lawrence in novels by Frederick Kohner.	14. Gidget
15.	Gertrude is Pocket Books' trademark. It's a . . .	15. Kangaroo
16.	Name the three Gabor sisters.	16. Zsa-Zsa, Eva, Magda
17.	General Sherman is considered to be the largest living thing in the world. What is it?	17. Sequoia tree
18.	This actress and singer's real name was Frances Gumm.	18. Judy Garland
19.	He was Dr. Frankenstein's crippled assistant in the 1931 movie.	19. Fritz
20.	This was Mr. Wilson's pet dog on TV's *Dennis the Menace*.	20. Freemont

Ph.D. Level

21.	This is the shuttle craft aboard the U.S.S. *Enterprise* on TV's *Star Trek*.	21. *Galileo*
22.	A ship with three rowing decks was called a . . .	22. Trireme
23.	This was Greta Garbo's first talkie.	23. *Anna Christie*
24.	John Glenn was the first American to orbit the earth. The capsule was named . . .	24. *Friendship 7*
25.	He was the Oriental villain in Sax Rohmer novels.	25. Fu Manchu
26.	She was the first female news broadcaster on a network news program.	26. Barbara Walters
27.	This was Jody's pony in John Steinbeck's *The Red Pony*.	27. Gabilan
28.	On TV this black stallion was owned by Joey Clark on the Broken Wheel Ranch.	28. Fury
29.	Hitler planned to rebuild Berlin and name it . . .	29. Germania
30.	Edward Richard was called Champion Cowboy of the World. He was better known as . . .	30. Hoot Gibson

Freshman Level

1. In *Gulliver's Travels* this was the land of the small people.
2. Li'l Abner lived here.
3. This dance was named in honor of Charles Lindbergh.
4. This was Guy Lombardo's band.
5. London Bridge was reerected in this state.
6. His nickname was Lonesome George.
7. Which hand is one better than a straight in poker?
8. Looney Tunes always ended their cartoons with this statement.
9. He was nicknamed the Louisville Lip.
10. This was Lucy's maiden name in *I Love Lucy*.

1. Lilliput
2. Dogpatch
3. Lindy Hop
4. Royal Canadians
5. Arizona
6. George Gobel
7. Flush
8. "That's All Folks"
9. Muhammad Ali
10. McGillicuddy

Graduate Level

11. Name the amusement park in the 1973 movie *West World*.
12. This was Alley Oop's pet dinosaur.
13. Lamb Chop is this ventriloquist's puppet.
14. The Statue of Liberty is on this island.
15. He wrote the *Lord of the Rings* trilogy.
16. Name two of the three books in the *Lord of the Rings* trilogy.

17. The number 3.14159265 is known as . . .
18. A stamp collector is called a . . .
19. In the zodiac what is the sign of the Archer called?
20. What does the word Luftwaffe mean in English?

11. Delos
12. Dino
13. Shari Lewis
14. Liberty Island
15. J. R. R. Tolkien
16. *Fellowship of the Ring*; *The Two Towers*; *The Return of the King*

17. Pi
18. Philatelist
19. Sagittarius
20. Air Weapon

Ph.D. Level

21. He was the American Navy officer in Puccini's *Madama Butterfly*.
22. What was the butler's name in *The Addams Family*?
23. Name the spirit in animal form that acts as a servant to a witch?
24. She is Loretta Lynn's sister.
25. This plant provides the basic ingredient of chocolate.
26. She is Warren Beatty's sister
27. Name the world's first postage stamp issued in Britain in 1840.
28. She taught school at Madison High.
29. Sentences or words that read the same backwards or forwards are called . . .
30. In 1983 he became the first Frenchman since 1946 to win the French Open (tennis).

21. Lieutenant Pinkerton
22. Lurch
23. Familiar
24. Crystal Gayle
25. Cacao tree
26. Shirley MacLaine
27. One Penny Black
28. Miss Brooks
29. Palindromes
30. Yannick Noah

Freshman Level

1. How many gold medals did Canada win at the 1976 Olympics in Montreal?
2. What do Rod Laver and Pancho Gonzales have in common?
3. What is the name of President Carter's daughter?
4. This product was purportedly "shot from guns."
5. He played the title role in *The Benny Goodman Story.*
6. What was Mohammed Reza Pahlavi better known as?
7. What was Belle Starr known for?

8. How many players are on a volleyball team?
9. With which sport is Sharif Khan identified?
10. Where is the world's largest rodeo held?

1. None
2. Tennis players
3. Amy
4. Quaker Puffed Wheat
5. Steve Allen
6. Shah of Iran
7. Female outlaw of Old West
8. Six
9. Squash
10. Calgary, Alberta, Canada

Graduate Level

11. Which state did Senator Hubert Humphrey represent?
12. What is the literal meaning of Dinosaur?
13. Steve Weed's girl friend was abducted. Who was she?
14. In which school did TV's Mr. Novak teach?
15. Pewter was originally an alloy of which two metals?
16. Which sport is represented by the Thomas Cup?
17. The Tour de France involves which sport?
18. What is the white ball called in billiards?
19. What is it called when the white ball goes into a pocket in pocket billiards?
20. What does the Roman numeral "D" represent?

11. Minnesota
12. Terrible Lizard
13. Patricia Hearst
14. Jefferson High
15. Tin and lead
16. Badminton
17. Bicycle racing
18. Cue ball
19. Scratch

20. 500

Ph.D. Level

21. Frank Morris was the first criminal to . . .
22. This was the name for the Shah of Iran's secret police.
23. In which year will Halley's Comet return
24. He directed the movie *North by Northwest.*
25. Which state excluding Alaska is nearest the North Pole?
26. Which sport uses these terms: cesta, pelotas, and fronton?
27. Which country developed Tae-Kwan-Do?
28. What was Susan Powell's claim to fame in 1981?
29. How many pairs of ribs does man have?
30. This former Tarzan hosted the 1980 Miss America Pageant.

21. Escape from Alcatraz
22. SAVAK
23. 1986
24. Alfred Hitchcock
25. Minnesota
26. Jai Alai
27. Korea
28. Miss America
29. Twelve
30. Ron Ely

Freshman Level

1. Moses received the Ten Commandments on this mountain.
2. The little people in *The Wizard of Oz* were called . . .
3. A woman, under hyponosis, said she was a girl living in Ireland in 1806. The girl's name was . . .
4. He hosted *The Newlywed Game*.
5. This city is billed as the Biggest Little City in the World.
6. This was Jack Klugman's role in *The Odd Couple*.
7. Who played Oscar Madison in the 1967 movie?
8. Who wrote the play *The Odd Couple*?
9. In which state would you find the geyser *Old Faithful*?
10. She was Popeye's girl friend.

1. Mount Sinai
2. Munchkins
3. Bridey Murphy
4. Bob Eubanks
5. Reno, Nevada
6. Oscar Madison
7. Walter Matthau
8. Neil Simon
9. Wyoming
10. Olive Oyl

Graduate Level

11. Diana Rigg portrayed her on TV. She was Steed's partner on *The Avengers*
12. Monday's child is fair of face, Tuesday's child is full of . . .
13. The poem "Casey at the Bat" takes place in this town.
14. Name the heroine of the play *Pygmalion*.
15. The recorded score of a forfeited football game is . . .
16. This was William Sidney Porter's pen name.
17. What do the interlocking Olympic rings represent?
18. This train ran from Paris, France, to Istanbul, Turkey.
19. The Oscar award holds a sword, but what does he stand on?
20. This *Seasame Street* muppet lives in a garbage can.

11. Mrs. Emma Peel
12. Grace
13. Mudville
14. Eliza Doolittle
15. 1—0
16. O. Henry
17. The five continents
18. Orient Express
19. A roll of film
20. Oscar the Grouch

Ph.D. Level

21. The Mutt and Jeff comic strip was created by . . .
22. This was the only movie in which Mae West and W. C. Fields appeared together.
23. If a baseball game is forfeited, the score is recorded as . . .
24. Name two of Noah's three sons.
25. What does a numismatist collect?
26. This was the name of the boat that was destroyed in the movie *Jaws*.
27. What was Eleanor Roosevelt's maiden name?
28. The annual awards given to animal performers in the movies are called . . .
29. P. F. Flyers were popular tennis shoes of the 1950's. What did the PF stand for?
30. What was the number of John F. Kennedy's torpedo boat which was sunk in the Solomons, World War II.

21. Bud Fisher
22. *My Little Chickadee*
23. 9 — 0
24. Ham, Shem, Japheth
25. Coins or medals
26. *Orca*
27. Roosevelt
28. Patsys
29. Posture Foundation
30. PT—109

Freshman Level

1. The Danube River flows into this sea.
2. He was the magician in King Arthur's court.
3. The Golden Wedding Anniversary celebrates how many years of marriage?
4. What is a ship's kitchen called?
5. David killed him with a sling.
6. How many stars are there in our Solar System?
7. The Moors invaded this European country in 711.
8. This animal is known as "polecat" in the U.S.A.
9. What is the fear of being closed in called?
10. Golf originated in this country.

1. Black Sea
2. Merlin
3. Fifty
4. Galley
5. Goliath
6. One (the sun)
7. Spain
8. Skunk
9. Claustrophobia
10. Scotland

Graduate Level

11. What is the Old Bailey?
12. He was the king of the Norse gods.
13. This is the national bird of New Zealand
14. Where is the Wailing Wall?
15. Whose dying words were, "Kiss Me, Hardy"?
16. This overture by Tchaikovsky has a date in its title.
17. Baleen Whales feed on this.
18. What is the criteria for belonging to the group known as MENSA?
19. The open area of the eye is known as the . . .
20. In Australia, stagnant backwaters are known as . . .

11. London's Central Criminal Court
12. Odin
13. Kiwi
14. Jerusalem
15. Horatio Nelson
16. "1812 Overture"
17. Plankton
18. High score on an intelligence test
19. Pupil
20. Billabongs

Ph.D. Level

21. Which country are Gurkhas from?
22. A dot placed after a note in music means what?
23. In Greek mythology he was Penelope's husband.
24. This volcano erupted violently in 1883.
25. Dick Turpin made his living as a . . .
26. The Lion Gate is preserved in this Greek City.
27. A solution of acetic acid is more commonly known as . . .
28. In this South American country women wear bowler hats.
29. What is the source of turpentine?
30. This opera by Gilbert and Sullivan was named after the Japanese Emperor.

21. Nepal
22. The length of the note is increased by half
23. Odysseus
24. Krakatoa, Indonesia
25. Highwayman
26. Mycenae
27. Vinegar
28. Bolivia
29. Coniferous trees
30. *The Mikado*

Freshman Level

1. She was King Arthur's wife.
2. How many millimeters in a meter?
3. Which gasoline had a flying red horse as its trademark?
4. This was Glenn Miller's theme song.
5. Her real name was Norma Jean.
6. Which planet has an orbit that sometimes carries it beyond Pluto?
7. MGM stands for . . .
8. Tonto often referred to the Lone Ranger by this name.
9. How much is four cubed?
10. How many red stripes are on the American flag?

1. Guinevere
2. 1,000
3. Mobil
4. "Moonlight Serenade"
5. Marilyn Monroe
6. Neptune
7. Metro-Goldwyn-Mayer
8. Kemo Sabe
9. Sixty-four
10. Seven

Graduate Level

11. Ornithology is the study of . . .
12. Where would you see this combination of letters: PNRD?
13. Name all the letters of the alphabet which have no straight lines in their formation.
14. How many of the twenty-six letters are formed from only straight lines in their formation.
15. The eggs of sturgeons.
16. Name Captain Kirk's ship on TV's *Star Trek*.
17. This was the man Jesus raised from the dead.
18. What is the twelve-month period between settlement of financial accounts called?
19. This is the home of TV's Yogi Bear.
20. These two magpies appeared in movie cartoons.

11. Birds
12. Automatic gear shift
13. O, C, S
14. Nine
15. Caviar
16. U.S.S. *Enterprise*
17. Lazarus
18. Fiscal year
19. Jellystone Park
20. Heckle and Jeckle

Ph.D. Level

21. This was a small lake where Henry David Thoreau lived from 1845 to 1847.
22. In which state is the Trinity Site (first atom bomb)?
23. Name an egg-laying mammal.
24. How many points are there on the leaf on the Canadian flag?
25. On March 4, 1974, her picture appeared on the cover of the first issue of *People* Magazine.
26. This fictitious Alabama town was the setting for the film *To Kill a Mockingbird*.
27. What do the letters in LASER stand for?

28. What does "La Cucaracha" mean?
29. Which country has a flag that is completely green?
30. In which state was the first McDonald's hamburger stand?

21. Walden Pond
22. New Mexico
23. Platypus, echidna
24. Eleven
25. Mia Farrow
26. Maycomb
27. Light Amplification by Stimulated Emission of Radiation
28. The Cockroach
29. Libya
30. California

Freshman Level

1. Who threw Brer Rabbit into the brier patch?
2. His nickname was Broadway Joe.
3. What subject did Mr. Chips teach?
4. Vinnie Barbarino and Arnold Horshack were in this TV series.
5. Who says, "Ah . . .what's up Doc"?
6. He played the lead in the movie, *Bullitt*.
7. This city is the capital of Bermuda.
8. This was Captain Queeg's ship.
9. This famous lover's last name was Capulet.
10. He was the original ninety-seven pound weakling.

1. Brer Fox
2. Joe Namath
3. Latin
4. *Welcome Back Kotter*
5. Bugs Bunny
6. Steve McQueen
7. Hamilton
8. U.S.S. *Caine*
9. Juliet
10. Charles Atlas

Graduate Level

11. This was the cargo of the H.M.S. *Bounty* at the time of the mutiny in 1789.
12. Name the four musicians in Grimms' "Bremen Town Musicians."
13. This movie, made for TV, was about former Chicago Bear Brian Piccolo, who died of cancer.
14. What was Mr. Chip's full name?
15. In which cartoon series did Gaylord the buzzard, Irwin the troll, and Earl the bat appear?
16. Which profession's symbol consists of a snake (or two) entwined on a rod?
17. This was the theme song of Paul Whiteman's band.
18. She was Julius Caesar's wife at the time of his death.
19. This is the boy's camp from which Allan Sherman writes home in his 1962 hit song, "Hello Muddah, Hello Faddah."
20. Captain Van Straaten was condemned to wander forever on the oceans of the world in this ship.

11. Breadfruit trees
12. Dog, cat, donkey, cock
13. *Brian's Song*
14. Arthur Chipping
15. *Broom Hilda*
16. Medical profession
17. "Rhapsody in Blue"
18. Calpurnia
19. Camp Granada
20. *Flying Dutchman*

Ph.D. Level

21. This bear lived with Pogo in the Okefenokee Swamp.
22. He was Ichabod Crane's rival for Katrina in "The Legend of Sleepy Hollow."
23. What school did Mr. Chips teach at?
24. In which novel do these brothers appear: Dmitri, Ivan, and Alyosha?
25. This classic hero was created in 1928 by P. Nowlan in a story titled, "Armageddon 2419 A.D."
26. Name two of the three writers for the Alan Brady Show on TV's *The Dick Van Dyke Show*.
27. This was Bill Sykes' dog in the movie *Oliver*.
28. This product was advertised on small boards spaced so they could be read sequentially by passing motorists.
29. This is the only U.S. National Monument that is mobile.
30. This was the TV series that featured Sgt. Ernie Bilko.

21. Bridgeport
22. Brom Bones
23. Brookfield
24. *The Brothers Karamazov*
25. Buck Rogers
26. Buddy Sorrell, Sally Rogers, Rob Petrie
27. Bullseye
28. Burma Shave
29. Cable cars
30. *You'll Never Get Rich*